MAORI MYTHS &
TRIBAL LEGENDS

MAORI MYTHS & TRIBAL LEGENDS

RETOLD BY ANTONY ALPERS

Illustrated by Patrick Hanly

Longman Paul

LONGMAN PAUL LIMITED
182–190 Wairau Road, Auckland 10, New Zealand

*Associated companies, branches and
representatives throughout the world*

*First published 1964
Reprinted 1972
Reprinted 1974
Reprinted 1975
Reprinted 1977
Reprinted 1980
Reprinted 1981
Reprinted 1982
Reprinted 1983
Reprinted 1985
Reprinted 1988
Reprinted 1989
Reprinted 1990
Reprinted 1991*

ISBN 0 582 71674 8

*Produced by Longman Paul Ltd
Printed in Hong Kong*

PREFACE

FROM Asia in the west, the ancestors of the Polynesians reached out across the bright Pacific to Tahiti and its neighbouring islands. In those green gardens of abundance they flourished and multiplied so greatly that in time they had to spread again. Parties, most probably of tribes defeated in quarrels over land and food, set out in canoes from the Marquesas, Tahiti, and other islands of Central Polynesia, to look for new homes. Some, sailing northward, found the Hawaiian islands, and their descendants are today American citizens. Others, being blown or sailing south and west, found the cooler and very much larger islands which they called Aotearoa, 'Long White Cloud', and their descendants are today New Zealanders—but are known as 'Maori', from their own word meaning 'a person of this place'. Their more austere, or at any rate less lush environment may have made them a little graver than their tropical cousins are today.

The Maori, like the Hawaiians, carried with them from the homeland a mythology that matched their own great qualities, yet whose elements can be traced back to the home of man himself, being obviously drawn from the ancient common stock of universal myth. Chaos, deluge, man's first sin, the fire theft—all these the Maori were found to have among their myths when at length the white man came upon them, together with a pantheon of gods and heroes who can be mentioned in the same breath as those of the Greeks, and a Creation myth, in fact, that rivals Genesis in beauty. In the meantime, following the ordeal of their migration and the adaptation of those who survived it to the new land and a new identity, they had added a store of splendid tribal histories, half fact, half legend, that record symbolically their tribal quarrels in the homeland over food, the epic journeys they made across the ocean to escape them—and their further tribal quarrels.

It is more than a hundred years now since these myths and legends were first collected. During that time Sir George Grey's *Polynesian Mythology*, which John Murray published in London in 1855, has deservedly become a sort of classic. Its preface admittedly contained some Western naïvetes. 'That their traditions are puerile is true,' wrote Grey. 'That the religious faith of the races who trust in them is absurd is a melancholy fact. But . . . the native races who believed in these traditions are in no way deficient in intellect, and in no respect incapable of receiving the truths of Christianity.' We must forgive Grey these credulities of his time. His book stands unchallenged as the best collection made from the unwritten literature of an island people whose life and ways and attitudes still fascinate the Western world. Inevitably, however, it has also gathered dust. Only with effort do we find it readable today, and many gaps, errors, and suppressions have become apparent. Meanwhile the most widely read new renderings, being intended for children, have had the effect of degrading the mythology to the merely fabulous and quaint.

This simply reflects a convention that is now very widely established. When the legends of primitive peoples are read for enjoyment it is almost always by the young. Adults may read *about* them, and scholars study them, but it is left for children to experience them; and yet they do not experience them, since we always soak the tales in milk before allowing them to be read. Especially has this been so with the myths of Polynesia. Adopting what is still essentially a missionary attitude, we have applied our classroom taboos and reduced them to pallid fantasy; while the illustrators, all too frequently, have degraded Polynesia's gods and heroes to a tribe of ludicrous hobgoblins, or brownies prancing about in the forest earning bushcraft badges. In this way we ensure that the stories can give no real impression of the lives and culture of those whose literature they originally were—and whose own children, of course, were brought up on them. What is worse though, we destroy the essence of the myth: we destroy its religious sense. Which is perhaps what we unconsciously intend: the people were savages, with no religion.

This book is an attempt to set things right. Both author and artist venture to hope that it may rescue the Maori myths from the children's bookshelf and make their richer qualities more widely known. The stories are therefore presented in current English, more or less, and in a modern form; and without retreating, because of the presence of youthful ears, from the undoubted harshness and great symbolic power of the originals.

The book is in two parts. The first contains the mythology proper of the Maori, those myths that he brought to New Zealand from 'Hawaiki'—the dimly remembered homeland from which he thought all men had sprung, and which no reader should try too hard to place on any map.★ In these the European, or American, or shall we say Christian reader will encounter

★'Hawaiki' is neither Tahiti nor Rarotonga nor any one part of Polynesia. It is the Maori form of the Polynesian word for 'homeland', and could refer to either of those dispersal points or to some other place not known. It has been appropriated (in the local dialect) as a place-name for Savaii, in Samoa, and for Hawaii. In the form Havai'i it was the old name for Ra'iatea, in French Polynesia—the island with the strongest claim to be the Hawaiki of the New Zealand Maori.

many familiar themes; for these stories simply constitute one of the myriad transplantings that were made, over millenniums of time, from the age-old stock of primitive man's mythology: one of the farthest flung of such transplantings, and also one of the most recent. As Joseph Campbell is currently demonstrating with new clarity in his masterly work *The Masks of God*, primitive myth arose and spread—along with and inextricably linked to man's material culture and his economy—from a nuclear seedbed of the Neolithic age somewhere in the Near East, as we call it, giving rise in due course to the mythologies of the high civilisations. Very much later—thousands of years, and also thousands of miles away from that centre of origin—the seeds of these myths were blown or sailed to the islands where they took their present form, as recently as ten centuries ago. So that here, in the clothing of the Maori imagination and against a background of the New Zealand bush and coast, we have all the elements of the universal myth. Not only chaos and deluge and the fire theft, but the creation of woman and man's first sin, the phallic serpent, the realm of the dead, cannibal ogress, resurrected hero, a version of the miracle of loaves and fishes, and that tremendous symbol the 'threshold passage' of the death-which-is-a-birth, all these occur in some guise in the stories of Part One, and remind us that wherever man carried his material culture— his weapons and tools, his use of fire, his hunting and planting ways— he also took his myths.

Part Two is a selection (no more than that) of the best canoe traditions, the fabulous histories by which the various Maori tribes laid claim to their lands and recorded their descent from certain ancestors in Hawaiki who, in turn, were descended from the gods and demi-gods we learn of in Part One. These have been chosen simply for their worth as stories, from those legends that chance selected for collection one hundred years ago, and chosen without regard for historical completeness or present-day tribal pride. One important story, for example—that of Toi and Whatonga, of the migration's 'second wave'—is missing altogether, merely for want of an original that does it justice as narrative.

There is more to be said about all these stories, their meaning, how they were collected, and how they have been treated here. This will come better at the end of the book, but there is one point touching all of them which probably needs to be explained before they are read. It concerns the Maori attitude to cooked food and to obscenity, or swearing; not to sex and obscenity (or to any function of the nether organs), but to *food* and obscenity.

If the moral attitudes of primitive man are hard for the Western mind to grasp and translate into familiar terms, there can hardly be one more so than the Maori notion of cooked food as the lowest thing, the furthest opposite from the sacred, in fact as filthy. For us to divest our minds of

Christian notions of good and evil and substitute the concept of simple payment, harm for harm (or 'revenge', as we commonly call it with a misleading moral overtone), is simple enough—perhaps because every schoolchild has at some time known the latter in his horrid heart. Even the Maori custom of weeping over friends when they *arrive* instead of when they depart⋆ has a certain logic that is not beyond our comprehension. But to enter, against all conditioning, into the minds of a people for whom cooked food and the act of eating could carry the overtones of meaning that we in our greater wisdom attach to their physical opposites and to sex, is a good deal harder. One has somehow to throw the mind into a state of being that is *radically* unlike ours. Yet if the trick can be done, a light comes on.

It is often remarked—and romantics invariably idealise the fact—that for the pre-missionary Polynesian the nouns and verbs connected with sex and the nether organs were in no way 'charged' as they are for us. No D. H. Lawrence was needed to cleanse the Polynesian mind. This does not mean that the Polynesian had no taboo expressions with which to release his violent thoughts. He had them all right (and Lawrence, it would seem, overlooked man's *need* of such taboos). But, for some reason which perhaps will ever elude us, they did not relate to what comes out of the body but to what goes into it—a straight reversal, like the weeping over friends returned.

One Maori myth, not included in this book, deals with the point expressly. Its subject is the danger of swearing, and especially of swearing at a deity like the moon. A woman named Rona, obliged to fetch water after dark, was going down to the stream by moonlight with a gourd. The moon went behind a cloud, she stumbled on a root, and cursed the moon with a violent oath—'You *cooked-head* of a moon!' It sounds merely quaint to us. But Rona had called the moon 'You——!' or something of that sort. In punishment, she was snatched up instantly to the moon itself, and there to this day she can still be seen, with her empty gourd.

In historical times also (we are told by the missionary Richard Taylor), whole feuds between Maori tribes began because of cursing of this kind, or even because of remarks dropped inadvertently. One man chanced to remark of a visiting chief of another tribe, who was sweating after running, that he looked like a steaming earth-oven. The remark was overheard—and began a war.

In the pages that follow, the reader will first encounter this point about food in the conflict of the gods following the Creation, where Tu (the god of war, and therefore man) eventually makes the progeny of all his brothers, except the wind-god, into food, and so *degrades* them, and makes

⋆See, for example, pages 80, 89, 110, and 214

them common. If this seems a mystery, a series of later and more specific references may make it less so. Rupe, when visiting Rehua, dares not partake of birds that have been feeding on the head-lice of a *god*. (There is nothing wrong with eating head-lice—they are a normal Polynesian delicacy to this day—but their sacredness in this instance makes eating them, even at second hand, unthinkable.) The first great tribal wars, once the golden age of the gods has ended, are triggered off by Kae's action, not in stealing, but in *eating* Tinirau's pet whale; and Kae himself is *eaten* in payment for this evil. In calling Whakatau's canoe-full of warriors a 'food bowl' the Ati Hapai deliver the ultimate and most degrading of insults to his men, and any young Maori listener to this tale would have known that only the most dreadful retribution could ensue. The quarrels that led to the Aotea and Arawa migrations from Hawaiki are both triggered off by acts of eating—each being returned in kind more horribly. Manaia's appalling curse against his sister's husband Ngatoro is a promise to make him frizzle on red-hot cooking stones—and so on, through to the cannibal orgies that climax the stories of Manaia and Hatupatu. It becomes plain that these, for the correct effect to be received by Western readers, should be mentally translated into, let us say, mass sexual orgies involving foreign soldiers and the female members of the family of a popular President or respected monarch. Anyone still puzzled, or who imagines that superior Western man has grown beyond the savage's taboos, might care to try, as a simple practical experiment, discussing this possibility further in explicit detail, in public.

To the Maori, then, a curse that invoked the filthiness of cooked food was the ultimate in insults, and had immense releasing power; and the Western reader, reading Maori myth or legend, is missing something essential until he can somehow feel, not merely calculate, this radical social difference. For it obviously throws light on the deeper significance of the cannibal act. The cannibal feast, as encountered in the stories in this book, could scarcely have been a simple sitting down to a welcome meal—however rare and appetising a dish of roast mammalian flesh may have been to the Maori, living in a land virtually without mammals. (There were only rats and dogs, both introduced, and a small species of bat, in Aotearoa.) Some other, grosser, joyless lust was surely involved. The Maori warrior, sweaty from the battle and squatting with his cuts and bruises beside a steaming umu to await his share of the hearts and livers of his enemy, was probably about as cheerful as some European soldier in his twenties raping nuns. For there are hints, from Polynesian history and in the accounts of converts, that feelings of guilt were not unknown. On one island in the Cook group, Mangaia, cannibalism had been renounced some generations before the arrival of the missionaries, and the chief who decreed it was revered. On the nearby island of Atiu, when Captain Cook made the first European contact and his officers inquired if human flesh was eaten there, the people denied it with a show of great disgust—but quite untruthfully, as missionaries later learned. The New Zealand Maori, too, was quick to abandon the practice and speak of it with shame, after Christian conversion; and has since had to substitute, after learning the associations, a different form of the ultimate obscenity.

A. A.

January 1965

CONTENTS

PART TWO: TRADITIONS OF THE MIGRATION

PART ONE

MYTHS FROM HAWAIKI

The beginning was made from the nothing

Rangi and Papa, the Sky father and the Earth mother, were the parents of all creation. The sons of these two were the elements of life, and one son, Tane, created the first woman.

THE SONS OF SKY AND EARTH

BEFORE there was any light there was only darkness, all was night. Before there was even darkness there was nothing. Of these things it is spoken in our karakia, those chants given down from ancient time that name all the ancestors of the Maori people. It is said in the karakia, at the beginning of time there stood Te Kore, the Nothingness. Then was Te Po, the Night, which was immensely long and immensely dark:

> Te Po nui,
> Te Po roa,
> Te Po uriuri,
> Te Po kerekere,
> Te Po tiwha,
> Te Po tangotango,
> Te Po te kitea . . .

meaning the Great Night, the Long Night, the Dark Night, the Intensely Dark Night, the Gloom-laden Night, the Night to be Felt, the Night Unseen. The first light that existed was no more than the glowing of a worm, and when sun and moon were made there were no eyes, there was none to see them, not even gods. The beginning was made from the nothing.

> From the nothing the begetting,
> from the nothing the increase,
> from the nothing the abundance,
> the power of increasing, the living breath:
> it dwelt with the empty space,
> it produced the sky which is above us.

The sky that floats above the earth,
great Rangi nui, the spread-out space,
dwelt with the red glow of dawn
and the moon was made;
the great sky above us
dwelt with the shooting rays
and the sun sprang forth,
they were thrown up above us as the
    chief eyes of heaven.
Then the heavens became light,
the early dawn,
the early day,
the mid-day,
the blaze of day from the sky.

Then Rangi nui, the Sky, dwelt with Papa tu a nuku, the Earth, and was joined to her, and land was made. But the offspring of Rangi and Papa, who were very numerous, were not of the shape of men, and they lived in darkness, for their parents were not yet parted. The Sky still lay upon the Earth, no light had come between them. The heavens were ten in number, and the lowest layer, lying on the Earth, made her unfruitful. Her covering was creeping plants and rank low weed, and the sea was all dark water, dark as night. The time when these things were seemed without end, as it is stated in the tradition:

From the first division of time unto the tenth, and to the hundredth, and to the thousandth, all was darkness. The black sky lay upon the earth and made her barren, and in vain did she seek her offspring in the likeness of the day, or of the night.

At length the offspring of Rangi and Papa, worn out with continual darkness, met together to decide what should be done about their parents, that man might arise. 'Shall we kill our parents, shall we slay them, our father and our mother, or shall we separate them?' they asked. And long did they consider in the darkness:

The night, the night,
the day, the day,
the seeking out, the adzing out
from the nothing, the nothing.
Their seeking thought also for their mother,
that man might arise.
Behold, this is the word,
the largeness, the length,
the height of their thought.

At last Tu matauenga, the fiercest of the offspring of Sky and Earth and the god of war, spoke out. Said Tu: 'It is well. Let us kill them.'

But Tane mahuta, god and father of the forests and all things that inhabit them, answered: 'No, not so. It is better to rend them apart, and to let the Sky stand far above us and the Earth lie below here. Let the Sky become a stranger to us, but let Earth remain close to us as our nursing mother.'

The other sons, and Tu the war god among them, saw wisdom in this and agreed with Tane, all but one. This one, that now forever disagreed with all his brothers, was the god and father of winds and storms, Tawhiri matea. Tawhiri, fearing that his kingdom would be overthrown, did not wish his parents to be torn apart. So while five sons agreed, Tawhiri was silent and would not, he held his breath. And long did they consider further. At the end of a time no man can measure the five decided that Rangi and Papa must be forced apart, and they began by turns to attempt this deed.

First Rongo ma Tane, god and father of the cultivated food of men, rose up and strove to force the heavens from the earth. When Rongo had failed, next Tangaroa, god and father of all things that live in the sea, rose up. He struggled mightily, but had no luck. And next Haumia tiketike, god and father of uncultivated food, rose up and tried, without success. So then Tu matauenga, god of war, leapt up. Tu hacked at the sinews that bound the Earth and

2

Sky, and made them bleed, and this gave rise to ochre, or red clay, the sacred colour. Yet even Tu, the fiercest of the sons, could not with all his strength sever Rangi from Papa. So then it became the turn of Tane mahuta.

Slowly, slowly as the kauri tree did Tane rise between the Earth and Sky. At first he strove with his arms to move them, but with no success. And so he paused, and the pause was an immense period of time. Then he placed his shoulders against the Earth his mother, and his feet against the Sky. Soon, and yet not soon, for the time was vast, the Sky and Earth began to yield. The sinews that bound them stretched and ripped. With heavy groans and shrieks of pain, the parents of the sons cried out and asked them why they did this crime, why did they wish to slay their parents' love? Great Tane thrust with all his strength, which was the strength of growth. Far beneath him he pressed the Earth. Far above he thrust the Sky, and held him there. As soon as Tane's work was finished the multitude of creatures were uncovered whom Rangi and Papa had begotten, and who had never known the light.

Now rose up Tawhiri, the god of winds and storms, who all this time had held his breath. Great anger moved him now, and this was Rangi's wish. Tawhiri, who feared that his kingdom would be overthrown, feared also that the Earth would become too fair and beautiful. For he was jealous now, jealous of all that Tane had procured. For Tane was the author of the day—

> Of the great day,
> of the long day,
> of the clear day,
> of the day driving away night,
> of the day making all things distinct,
> of the day making everything bright,
> of the day driving away gloom,
> of the hot, sultry day,
> of the day shrouded in darkness.

Tawhiri turned on Tangaroa

And so Tawhiri followed Rangi to the realm above, and consulted with him there. And with his father's help Tawhiri begot his numerous turbulent offspring, the winds and storms. He sent them off between the Sky and the Earth, one to the south, another to the east, another to the north-east. Then, in his anger, and remembering Rangi's wish, he sent the freezing wind, the burning dusty wind, the rainy wind, the sleety wind, and with them all the different kinds of clouds. Most powerful of all, Tawhiri himself came down like a hurricane, and placed his mouth to that of Tane, and shook his branches and uprooted him. The giant trees of Tane's forests groaned and fell, and lay on the earth to rot away, and became the food of grubs.

When his fury had dealt with Tane, Tawhiri turned on Tangaroa the sea god. From the forests he swept on down to the sea and lashed it in his rage. He heaved up waves as high as cliffs and whipped their crests away, he churned the sea to whirlpools, he battled with the tides, till Tangaroa took flight in terror from his usual home, the shores, and hid in the ocean depths, where Tawhiri could not reach him.

As Tangaroa was about to leave the shores, his grand-children consulted together as to how they might save themselves. For Tangaroa had begotten Punga, and Punga had begotten Ika tere, the father of fish, and Tu te wanawana, the father of lizards and reptiles. These two could not agree where it was best to go to escape the storms. Tu te wanawana and his party, shouting into the wind, cried 'Let us all go inland,' but Ika tere and his party cried 'No, let us go to the sea.' Some obeyed one and some obeyed the other, and so they escaped in two parties. Those of Tu te wanawana hid themselves on land, and those of Ika tere in the sea. This is what is called, in the ancient traditions of our people, 'The Separation of Tawhiri matea', and it is put in this fable:

The Shark was for going to the sea, but the Lizard was for going inland. Shark warned Lizard, 'Go inland, and the fate of your race will be that when they catch you and before they cook you, they will singe your skins off over a lighted wisp of fern.' Lizard answered, 'Go to the sea, and the fate of your race will be that when they serve out baskets of food to each person, you will be laid on top to give a relish to it.'

So they fled their separate ways, the fishes in confusion to the sea, and the lizards and reptiles to the little hiding places in the forests and the rocks. And for this reason Tangaroa, enraged that some of his offspring deserted him and were sheltered by the forests, has ever since made war on Tane, who in return has helped those who are at war with Tangaroa. So the sea is forever eating at the edges of the land, hoping that the forest trees will fall and become his food, and he consumes the trees and houses that are carried down to him by floods.

The separation of the fishes and the reptiles

When Tawhiri had done with Tangaroa he returned to the land again and fell upon his two most peaceful brothers, on Rongo and Haumia, the gods of cultivated and uncultivated food. But Papa, the Earth Mother, to save them for her other children, snatched them away and hid them in safe places. And so well did she protect these children, the sweet potato and the fern root, that Tawhiri pursued them in vain.

Tawhiri, having attacked four of his brothers, determined next to try his strength with Tu the war god, and rushed against him. Tawhiri stormed and howled, but Tu withstood him, for he placed his feet securely on the breast of the Earth his mother, and was safe. Thus Tu alone, the only one of the party who had been for murdering their parents, stood upright and unshaken. And so at last Tawhiri let his winds die down, and Rangi ceased to urge him on. Their rage was spent, and peace was in the space between the Earth and Sky.

But now the savage mood came over Tu the war god, wrath of man. Since Tane and the other three had left him to withstand Tawhiri on his own, he felt a wish to injure Tane. Besides, he knew that Tane's offspring were increasing and were making the earth more lovely, and he feared that they might become his enemies. He therefore gathered some of the long stringy leaves of the ti whanake tree and twisted them into nooses, and when he had made enough he went into the forest setting snares, and hung them in cunning ways. Soon the offspring of Tane were caught in his snares and lay trembling, unable to fly away, and became his food.

Next, Tu took revenge on Tangaroa for being no help to him against Tawhiri. He sought out the sea god's offspring, and found them leaping and swimming in the water. He cut down strips of Tane's flax and wove them into nets, and dragged them in the sea and hauled out Tangaroa's children. And he cooked them, and made them common, and ate them.

After that he took revenge on the meekest of his brothers, Rongo and Haumia. He found them by their tell-tale leaves, which still show man where food is growing. From a stout piece of one of Tane's trees he shaped a digging-stick, or ko, and with some flax he plaited baskets, and dug up the children of Rongo and Haumia, and by cooking them desanctified them and made them common, and he ate them.

His four brothers of the earth and sea, Tu had now defeated entirely, and their offspring were his food. But Tawhiri he could not defeat nor make into food. And so Tawhiri matea, the last-born of the children of Sky and Earth, remains as an enemy for man today, and both are eternally at war.

Thus Tu, the god of war, is man, but only the spirit and not the body, for man was not yet made, there being no woman. It was

Tane the husband, not Tu the warrior, who put this right. He took some earth and made the body of a woman. It was the red earth that is found at Kurakawa, red with the blood of the sinews that once joined Rangi and Papa. Tane fashioned the form of woman from this earth and breathed life into its nostrils. She was Hine ahu one, the Earth-formed Maid. She bore Tane a daughter, whose name was Hine titama, the Dawn Maid. And Hine titama grew up, and was beautiful, and in the course of time she also bore several daughters, who were the daughters of Tane.

One day Hine titama asked Tane who her father was. For answer he told her: 'Ask the posts of the house', and then she knew the truth. The man she thought of as her husband was her father. When she knew this, Hine titama was overwhelmed with shame. She resolved at once to leave the world of light, Te Ao, and retire to Te Po, the world below.

'O Tane, it is clear to me now,' she said. 'It is you who have brought me to this shame. I shall go and take refuge with my grandmother, Papa. The path I take shall be laid down for all time as the path to the underworld and I shall live there for ever.'

And so she went to Rarohenga, and the path of death was created, which since that time mankind has trodden ceaselessly. By means of powerful incantations Hine caused her children to go into a deep sleep, and, having weakened Tane so that he could not follow her, she went to the entrance of the world below. There she found Kuwatawata, the guardian of the entrance, who asked her where she was going. When she told him he said: 'Turn back, before it is too late. All light and all pleasure lie behind you, the spirit world is before you.' But Hine replied: 'No, I go to Rarohenga, the realm of the unknown, so that I can protect the welfare of my children of the upper world.'

As she went she turned around, and saw Tane following her, weeping as he came. 'Go back, Tane,' she cried. 'Go back to the light and raise our children. Let me stay here to gather them in.'

And so she passed through the entrance to the world below, to take up her endless task.

As from that time, she discarded the name of Hine titama and was known as Hine nui te Po, Great Hine the Night.

Every day, because of her, the dawn rises in the east and descends again in the west, and Tane follows her; and all men must follow her eternally, down the path she chose to take.

Now the names of the principal children of the Sky and Earth have these meanings:

Tane means the forests, and the birds and insects that live in them, as well as all things made of wood, or flax, or grass.

Tangaroa means fish of every kind, and crabs and mussels, sea-eggs, and eels, and all the food that man gets from the sea.

Rongo ma Tane means the kumara or sweet potato, and all plants that are cultivated by man for his food.

Haumia tiketike means the fern root and all other wild plants that give men food, such as berries and sow-thistle and certain toadstools and other fruits.

Tawhiri matea means all winds and storms.

And Tu is war, but also man.

When Tu had completed the conquest of all his brothers he assigned certain karakia to each of them. These chants were prayers or spells to make their offspring plentiful for his food. There were chants proper to Tane, chants for Tangaroa, for Rongo and for Haumia. There were chants also to Tawhiri to give favourable winds, and chants to Rangi to give fair weather; and to Papa, the Earth, to produce all things in abundance. There were also chants for man himself, suited to the different occasions in his life: chants for the naming of an infant, for protection against sickness, and for strength and victory in war. And chants for all of his belongings, for his houses and fortifications, his spears and his war clubs.

Up to the present time Rangi, the Sky, has remained separate

Much of the land was covered by the sea

from his wife, the Earth. But their love never diminished, and Rangi at the beginning shed an immense quantity of tears. So great was this weeping that much of the land that had been dry was covered by the sea, and there were countries underneath where a strange people lived who could not endure the sun; if they felt its rays they died.

At length, lest all the land be lost, a party of the other sons of Rangi and Papa resolved to turn their mother over, so that she and Rangi should not be always seeing one another's grief and grieving more. This was done, and is called Te hurihanga a Mataaho, the Overturning of Mataaho, after the son who saw to its being done. In consequence of this, Rangi's tears are less copious than they formerly were, when all the world was flooded. They are now the

To keep him warm Ruaumoko was given fire

dew drops that form in the night on Papa's back. The morning mists, that form in the valleys, are her sighs.

When Papa was turned over by Mataaho, Ruaumoko was still at her breast, and he remained there and was carried to the world below. To keep him warm there he was given fire. He is the god of earthquakes, and the rumblings that disturb this land are made by him as he walks about. According to some he is the husband of Hine nui te Po.

From the time of the separation of Rangi and Papa clear light increased upon the earth, and all the beings that had been hidden in the dark now multiplied and spread, and the descendants of Tane and Hine titama became the generations of men, and man increased and multiplied, and death did not have power over him until was reached the generation of Maui and his brothers. It was only after the demi-god Maui tikitiki a Taranga had attempted to violate Hine nui te Po that death had the power over man which it now has.

This is the narrative about the generations of the ancestors of men from the beginning of the Po, and therefore we, the people of this land, carefully preserved these traditions of old times as a thing to be taught to the generations that come after us. So we repeat them in our prayers and whenever we relate the deeds of the ancestors from whom each tribe and family is descended, and on other similar occasions.

Pay attention now to the stories that relate the
life of the demi-god Maui, the maker of mischief,
known as Maui tikitiki a Taranga.

HOW MAUI WAS BORN

MAUI was the fifth and youngest of his parents' sons, yet when he was born his brothers knew nothing of it. They first learned that they had a brother when he was discovered one night standing behind them in the great meeting house. Everyone was present, the four brothers, their mother Taranga, and all the relations, and there was dancing going on, when little Maui crept into the house unseen, and went and sat behind his brothers. When it came to their turn to dance, and their mother stood them up and counted them so as to be ready, he stood up with them.

'One, that's Maui mua; two, that's Maui roto; three, that's Maui taha; four, that's Maui pae,' she said; these names mean Maui the first, Maui the middle, Maui the side, and Maui the edge. Then she saw this other child standing with them, and cried out, 'Hullo, where did this one come from?' 'I'm your child too,' Maui replied. So she counted them again and said, 'Oh no, there ought to be only four of you. This is the first I've seen of *you.*' And so there was a scene, with little Maui and the old woman arguing about it in the middle of the rows of dancers. In the end she became annoyed with him. 'Now come on, out of the house!' she said. 'You are no child of mine, you belong to someone else. Go home!'

But little Maui stood up for himself. 'Well then, I'd better go, I suppose,' he said. 'Since you say so, I must be someone else's child. But I did think I was yours, because I know I was born at the edge of the sea, and you cut off a tuft of your hair and wrapped me in it and threw me in the waves. After that the seaweed took care of me and I drifted about in the sea, wrapped in long tangles of

'I'm your child too'

kelp, until a breeze blew me on shore again, and some jelly-fish
rolled themselves around me to protect me on the sandy beach.
Clouds of flies settled on me and I might have been eaten up by the
maggots; flocks of seabirds came, and I might have been pecked
to pieces. But then my great-ancestor Tama nui ki te rangi arrived.
He saw the clouds of flies and all the birds, and he came and
pulled away the jelly-fish, and there was I, a human being! Well,
he picked me up and washed me and took me home, and hung me
in the rafters in the warmth of the fire, and he saved my life.
And I grew, and eventually I heard about the dancing you have
here in this house, and that is what brought me here tonight.'

Now Taranga listened to all this in amazement. For in the custom
of our people, if a child was born before it finished growing in its
mother's womb and died without knowing any of the pleasures of
life, it was supposed to be buried with special prayers and ceremonies, otherwise it became a kind of evil spirit, always doing

mischief to the human race and hurting them out of spite, because of having missed the happiness that they enjoy. All the evil spirits had a beginning of this sort. So Maui was a little demi-god of mischief. The story he had told was true, and as his mother listened she remembered it all.

'From the time I was in your womb,' Maui went on, 'I have known the names of these children of yours. Listen,' he said, as he pointed to his brothers in turn. 'You are Maui mua, you are Maui roto, you are Maui taha, and you are Maui pae. And as for me, I am Maui potiki, Maui-the-last-born. And here I am.'

When he had finished, Taranga had to wipe her eyes because there were tears in them, and she said: 'You are indeed my last-born son. You are the child of my old age. When I had you, no one knew, and what you have been saying is the truth. Well, as you were formed out of my topknot you can be Maui tikitiki a Taranga.'

So that became his name, meaning Maui-formed-in-the-topknot-of-Taranga. And this is very strange, because women in those days did not have topknots. The topknot was the most sacred part of a person, and only men had them.

Then Maui did some of his magic things in front of his brothers and all the assembled people, and they were amazed.

After the dancing was over that evening and the sleeping-mats were unrolled, Taranga called her last-born child to her mat. 'Come here, child, and sleep with your mother,' she said. So when everyone else was settling down to sleep, Maui lay beside his mother on her sleeping-mat, and she pulled a cloak over them, and he curled up with her arm around him.

This made his elder brothers jealous, especially the two younger ones, and in the morning they were muttering about it. 'Look at that,' they said. 'Our mother never asks *us* to go and sleep with her, and yet we are the children there is no doubt about, we are the ones she actually saw born. Why, when we were little she nursed and fed us, and played with us on those mats of hers. She was fond of us then, but she doesn't treat us like that now, and never asks us to sleep beside her. As for this little abortion—who can tell whether he was really nursed by the sea-tangles, as he says, or whether he isn't someone else's child, who is now sleeping with our mother? Who would believe that a little object like that, tossed into the sea and forgotten, would turn up as a human being? And now he has the cheek to call himself a relation of ours!'

The two younger ones were going on about it like this, but the two older ones said: 'Never mind. Let him be our brother. Remember the proverb: *In time of war, settle your disputes by force, but in time of peace let things be done in a friendly way.* Let us be careful not to be like the children of Rangi and Papa, who once talked of killing their parents. Remember all the quarrelling *that* led to, and try not to let the same thing happen to us.' The younger ones decided that their brothers were right, and stopped their grumbling. And so Maui was accepted as their brother, and he slept beside his mother every night.

Now every morning at daybreak, Taranga used to wake up before her children and leave the house, and vanish until night. The older brothers were used to this, they knew that their mother was there at night but gone in the morning, but little Maui was not used to it and he found it very annoying. At first he thought in the mornings, 'Well, perhaps she has only gone to prepare some food for us.' But no, she really was gone, she was far away.

In the evening, when her children were all singing and dancing in the meeting house as usual, she used to return. And after the dancing she called young Maui to her sleeping-mat, and this happened every night. And as soon as the daylight came she disappeared again.

One day Maui asked his brothers to tell him where their mother and father lived. He said he wanted to visit them. They said they did not know. 'How can *we* tell?' they said. 'We don't know whether they live up there somewhere, or down below, or over there.'

'Well, never mind,' said Maui, 'I'll find them for myself.'

'Nonsense,' they said, 'how can you tell where they are, you, the youngest of all of us, when we ourselves don't know? After that first night when you turned up in the meeting house and made yourself known to us all, you know that our mother slept here every night, and as soon as the sun rose she went away, and she came back at evening, and this is how it always is. How can we tell where she goes?'

Now when Maui had this conversation with his brothers he had already discovered something for himself. During the previous night, as his mother and brothers were all sleeping, he had crept out and stolen his mother's skirt, her woven belt, and her warm, feathered cloak, and had hidden them. Then he had taken various garments and stopped up all the chinks around the doorway of the house and of its single wooden window, so that the first light of day would not get in and Taranga would not wake in time to go. When that was done he could not sleep. He was afraid his mother would wake up in the dark and spoil the trick. But Taranga did sleep on.

When the first faint light appeared at the far end of the house, Maui could see the legs of all the other people sleeping, and his mother was sleeping too. Then the sun came up, and Taranga stirred, and partly woke. 'What kind of night is this,' she wondered, 'that lasts so long?' But because it was dark in the house she dozed off again. At last she woke up properly, and knew that something was wrong. She threw off the cloak that covered her and jumped up, with nothing on, and went round looking for her skirt and belt. Little Maui pretended to be fast asleep.

Taranga rushed to the door, and the window beside it, and pulled out all the things that Maui had used to stop them up. When she saw that the sun was already in the sky she muttered some angry things and hurried out, holding in front of her a piece of old flax cloak that Maui had used to stop up the door. Away she ran, crying and whimpering at being so badly treated by her children.

Hei Tiki

No sooner was she out of the house than little Maui was on his knees behind the sliding door, which she had closed behind her as she left. He was watching to see which way she went. Not far away he saw her stop and pull up a clump of rushes. There was a hole under it, which she dropped into. She pulled the rushes into place behind her, and was gone. Maui slipped out and ran as fast as he was able to the clump of rushes. He pulled it and it came away, and he felt a wind against his face as he looked through the hole. Looking down, he saw another world, with trees and the ocean, and fires burning, and men and women walking about. He put the rushes back, and returned to the house and woke his brothers, who were all still fast asleep.

'Come on, come on! Wake up!' he cried. 'Here we are, tricked by our mother again!' So they all got up, and realised from the height of the sun that they had overslept.

That was the day when Maui asked them to tell him where his parents lived. He did not admit what he had seen that morning. And they said they did not know, and *he* would never know either.

'What does it matter to you, anyway?' they said. 'Do we care about our father or our mother? Did she feed us and look after us until we grew up? Not a bit of it. She went off every morning, just like this. Our true father, without any doubt, is great Rangi the Sky, whose offspring provide us with trees for our houses and birds and fishes for us to eat, and sweet potatoes and fern root. And who was it that sent those other offspring down to help us— Touarangi, the rain that waters our plants, Hau ma rotoroto, the fine weather that enables them to grow, Hau whenua, the soft winds that cool them, and Hau ma ringiringi, the mists that keep them moist? Did not Rangi give us all of these to make our food grow, and did not Papa make the seeds sprout in the earth? You know all this.'

'I certainly do know it all,' said Maui. 'In fact I know it far better than you do. For I was nursed and fed by the sea-tangles, whereas you four were nursed at our mother's breast. It could not have been until after she weaned you that you ate the foods you speak of, whereas I have never tasted either her milk or her cooking. Yet I love her, because I once lay in her womb. And because I love her, I want to find out where she and our father live, and go and see them.'

The other four were astonished when they heard their little brother speak like this. When they recovered themselves and were able to keep their faces straight, they glanced at one another and decided that they might as well let him have his way, and go to find their parents.

Now Maui had already performed some of his magic for them on the night when they first set eyes on him, in the meeting house. On that occasion, in front of all his relations, he had transformed himself into all kinds of birds that live in the forest. None of the shapes he assumed had pleased them particularly then, but now he turned himself into a kereru, or wood pigeon, and with this they were delighted.

'Heavens!' they said. 'You do look handsome. Much more beautiful than the birds you showed us last time.' What made him look so splendid now was that he was wearing the belt and skirt he had stolen from his mother that morning. The thing that looked so white across the pigeon's breast was his mother's belt. He also had the sheen of her skirt, that was made of burnished hair from the tail of a dog, and it was the fastening of her belt that made the beautiful feathers at his throat. This is how the wood pigeon got its handsome looks.

Maui now perched on the branch of a tree near his brothers, and there, just like a real kereru, he sat quite still in one place. He did not hop from bough to bough like other birds, but sat there cooing to himself. Which made his brothers coin our proverb, 'The stupid pigeon sits on *one* bough and does not hop from place to place.' And they went away, and left him to change his shape again.

Next morning Maui prepared to set off in search of his parents.

Before he left, he astonished his older brothers once again by making quite a speech.

'Now you stay here,' said little Maui, 'and you'll be hearing something of me after I am gone. It is because I love my parents so much that I am going off to look for them. Listen to me, and say whether the things I have been doing are remarkable or not. Changing into birds can only be done by someone who is skilled in magic, yet here am I, younger than all of you, and I have turned myself into all the birds of the forest, and now I am going to take the risk of growing old and losing my powers because of the great length of the journey to the place where I am going.'

'That might be so,' said his brothers, 'if you were going on some warlike expedition. But in fact you are only going to look for those parents whom we all love, and if you ever find them we shall all be happy. Our present sadness will be a thing of the past, and we shall spend our lives between this place and theirs, paying them happy visits. What is there to be afraid of?'

Little Maui went on, very serious: 'It is certainly a very good cause that leads me to undertake this journey, and when I reach the place I am going to, if I find everything agreeable, then I shall be pleased with it, and if I find it disagreeable, then I shall be disgusted with it.'

The brothers kept straight faces, and replied: 'What you say is exceedingly true, Maui. Depart then, on your journey, with your great knowledge and your skill in magic.' Then their brother went a little way into the forest, and came back in the shape of a pigeon once more, with his sheeny back and his white breast and his bright red eye. His brothers were charmed, and there was nothing they could do but admire him, as he flew away.

Until he found out where his mother and father
lived Maui had not been named nor put under
the protection of the gods. By a trick he dis-
covered where their home was, and there became
a man.

HOW MAUI FOUND HIS PARENTS

AWAY flew Maui in his pigeon shape, with his brothers admiring him as he went. But as soon as he was out of sight he wheeled about, and flew to the clump of rushes that marked the place where his mother disappeared. He came down, in his noisy pigeon way, and strutted about for a moment. Then he lifted the rushes. He flopped into the hole and replaced the clump behind him, and was gone. A few strokes of his wings took him to that other country, and soon he saw some people talking to one another on the grass beneath some trees. They were manapau trees, a kind that grows in that land and nowhere else. Maui flew down to the tops of the trees and, without being noticed by any of the people, perched on a branch that enabled him to see them. Almost at once he recognised Taranga, sitting on the grass beside her husband, a man who by his dress and demeanour was plainly a chief. 'Aha,' he cooed to himself, 'there are my father and my mother just below me.' And soon he knew that he was not mistaken, for he heard their names when other members of the party spoke to them. He flopped down through the leaves and perched on the branch of a puriri tree that had some berries on it. He turned his head this way and that, and tilted it on its side. Then he pecked off one of the berries and gently dropped it, and it hit his father's forehead.

'Was that a bird, that dropped that berry?' one of the party asked. But the father said No, it was only a berry that fell by chance. So Maui picked some more berries, and this time he threw them down quite hard, and they hit both the father and the mother and actually hurt them a little. Then everyone got up and walked round peering into the branches of the tree. The pigeon cooed, and everyone saw it. Some went away and gathered stones, and all of them, chiefs and common people alike, began throwing stones up into the branches. They threw for a long time without hitting the pigeon once, but then a stone that was thrown by Maui's father struck him. It was Maui, of course, who decided that it should, for unless he had wished it, no stone could have struck him. It caught his left leg, and down he fell, fluttering through the branches to the ground. But when they ran to pick the bird up, it had turned into the shape of a young man.

The people drew back, frightened. They saw his glaring eyes, bright red, not like a pigeon's now but red, as if they had been painted with ochre, the sacred colour.

'No wonder he sat there so long,' said one of the party. 'If he had been a bird he would have flown off long ago. But it is not a bird, it is a man.'

'No, that is not a man,' said one of the others. 'There has never been anything like that seen in this place.' He moved a little closer. 'Just look at the shape of him,' he said. 'He is something to do with the gods. Nothing like this has been seen since Rangi and Papa were torn apart.'

Then Taranga came forward and had a look at Maui. 'I used to see someone who looked like this person every night when I went to visit my children,' she said; and Maui noticed how she seemed to regard her visits as something that happened long ago, whereas he himself had seen her that very morning.

'Listen,' said Taranga to the other people, in a strange voice that was not like her voice at home. 'Once I was walking by the beach, and the pains came on. I was alone, and there on the beach I gave birth prematurely to one of my children. I thought that no one would ever know, and I unwound my topknot and cut off some of my hair, and wrapped the little creature in it, and threw him into

Maui flew down to the tops of the trees

the sea. But later he was found there by his ancestor Tama nui ki te rangi.'

The people were hushed, and they gathered closer, as Taranga unfolded the rest of her story. But Maui could hear that she told it almost in the words that he had used himself. When the story was ended, Taranga stepped forward to Maui, who was now sitting up. 'Where do you come from?' she asked him. 'From the west?'

'No.'

'From the north-east, then?'

'No.'

'From the south-east, then?'

'No.'

'From the south, then?'

'No.'

'Was it the wind which blows upon my cheek that brought you here?'

'Yes.'

'Then this is indeed my child,' Taranga cried. And she asked him: 'Are you Maui mua?'

'No.'

'Are you Maui roto?'

'No.'

'Are you Maui tikitiki a Taranga?'

He answered 'Yes,' and Taranga cried 'Aue!' and threw up her hands, and wailed again. 'This is indeed my child,' she cried. 'He was nursed by the waves and the sea-tangles, and became a human being after all. Welcome, my child, welcome to this place!' And her eyes flashed as she spoke these words:

'Some day the very threshold of your great ancestress Hine nui te Po shall be crossed by you. And when that happens death shall be vanquished, and will have no power over man.'

Then she took him to Makea tutara, her husband, saying: 'This is my youngest child, whom I have brought here for you.'

'What is his name?' the old man asked.

'He is called Maui tikitiki a Taranga.'

'That is the name of a great warrior,' said Makea. 'It is the name of one who is marked out to perform many bold and marvellous feats. He will be the sort that has no regard for dangers.'

Then Makea took Maui's hand and made him sit before him. And he passed his aged hands gently over Maui's head and body, and all the way down over his legs.

'This child has indeed an ill-formed, flattened head, but his body is strong, and his eyes are the red eyes of a fine warrior,' he said.

Then Maui was taken by his father to the tohi ceremony to be dedicated to the gods. Water was sprinkled over him with a branch of karamu leaves and incantations were said to make him sacred and protect him. But at the end of the ceremony Makea tutara felt a shudder go through him, which he knew was sent by the gods. He remembered that by mistake he had left out a part of one of the prayers. He knew that the gods were certain to punish this fault, and that in consequence of it Maui would have to die, he would not conquer death, and what Taranga had said would happen would not happen now, because of his mistake. To hide his agitation he went away from the other people a little distance and he chanted an invocation while he wept. For the old man foresaw then all that Maui would accomplish, to his own undoing. So great was Makea's grief that he would not go inside his house until it was evening.

Afterwards, Maui returned from that country to his brothers and told them that he had found out where their parents lived.

Before the events that are related in this story, Maui possessed the power of changing his own shape, but commanded no enchantment over other things or over nature. After he had obtained the jawbone of Muri ranga whenua he was able to perform great deeds for the benefit of man.

HOW MAUI OBTAINED THE SACRED JAWBONE

SOON after he had found where his parents lived Maui carried off and slew his first victim. She was the daughter of Maru te whare aitu, and when he had dealt with her in a brutal fashion he dealt with her father also. By means of enchantments he caused this old man's crops to wither, and they were all destroyed.

He then decided to make another visit to his parents, and this time he remained for a while in the country of the manapau trees. One day he noticed that some people were in the habit of carrying to a certain place some kono, or small baskets of food, for some old person.

'Who is that food for?' he asked them, and one of the people who were going with it answered: 'It is for your ancestress Muri ranga whenua.'

'Where does she live?' he asked, and they answered, 'Over there.'

'All right,' he said. 'That will do now. Leave the kono here. I will take them to her myself.'

From that time on Maui himself carried the daily presents of food that were meant for that old woman. But he never gave them to her, he merely went towards the place where she lived and hid the food in the bushes, and this he did for many days.

At length the old chieftainess realised that there was some mischief going on, and the next time Maui came by she put her nose in the air and sniffed. She sniffed and sniffed, feeling sure that there was food not far away. By now she was greatly exasperated by her many days of hunger, and her stomach began to swell out, ready to eat up Maui as soon as he came within reach. Leaning on her stick the old woman turned towards the south, and sniffed the air, but no scent of food or man could she detect. She turned her nose round slowly to the east, and then to the north, sniffing carefully at every angle. Still no scent of food or man could she detect, and she would have devoured either, instantly. She almost thought she must have been mistaken, but then she turned to the west for one more try. From the west, the scent of a man came plainly to her nose, and she cried: 'I know from the smell in this breeze that someone is close to me.' As she began to feel about her with her stick Maui murmured something, and she knew at once that he was a descendant of hers. Her stomach, which had been distended to a great size, began to shrink again. This was fortunate for Maui. If his scent had not been carried to that old woman's nose by the westerly breeze, she would certainly have eaten him up.

When her stomach had resumed its normal size the old woman asked him, 'Are you Maui?' and he answered in a respectful voice: 'Even so.' Then she drew near and peered at him with her eyes that were nearly blind. 'Why did you cheat your old ancestress like that?' she said. 'Why have you been hiding my dinner, so that I have had nothing to eat these many days?' And she pointed with a crooked finger to her toothless and empty mouth. 'Ei?' she asked, and poked young Maui with her finger.

In a voice that showed he was not in the least afraid of her, Maui answered: 'I was anxious that your jawbone, which has magic properties, should be given to me.'

'Take it,' said that old woman. 'It has been kept for you till now.'

So saying she took her jawbone—for she was dead all down one side from being starved—and handed it to Maui. He carried

it to the stream to wash off the blood and the bits of rotten flesh, and the blood went into the kokopu, giving that fish its reddish colour. After this he returned with the jawbone to the place where his brothers lived.

Soon afterwards Maui took a wife, and this led to the first of the exploits that he performed with the help of the jawbone of his ancestress. His wife went one day to wash herself in a still stream, and while she was in the water Tuna roa, the ancestor of eels, came slithering around her and made himself objectionable. That is, he touched her most improperly. When she went home she said to Maui: 'There is a man in that pool with very smooth skin.'

Maui at once felt jealous and decided to kill Tuna. He dug a trench beside the pool, and laid down nine logs as skids, so that Tuna might slide over them as when a canoe is launched. Then he told his wife to sit near the trench while he put up a screen to hide himself. Soon Tuna was seen swimming towards her, and as he slithered over the skids Maui ran out and slew him with the enchanted weapon. One end of Tuna went into the sea and became the ngoiro, or conger eel. The other end became the fresh-water eel and is still called tuna. A part of him became the kareao, or supple-jack, whose smooth black canes, like eels among the river-weed, entangle the forest undergrowth today. And the blood of Tuna was absorbed by the rimu, the totara, and other trees, giving their wood its reddish colour.

After this exploit Maui lived quietly with his wife, and children were born to them.

She took her jawbone and handed it to Maui

Before the events that are related in this story the days were shorter than they are and the nights were longer. Maui, with the help of his brothers, altered this to man's advantage.

HOW MAUI MADE THE SUN SLOW DOWN

ONE day Maui said to his wife: 'Light a fire and cook some food for me.' She did so, but no sooner had she heated her cooking stones in the earth-oven than the sun went down, and they had to eat their food in the dark. This set Maui to thinking how the days might be made longer. It was his opinion that they were shorter than they needed to be, and that the sun crossed the sky too quickly. So he said to his brothers: 'Let us catch the sun in a noose and make him move more slowly. Then everybody would have long days in which to get their food and do all the things that have to be done.'

His brothers said it was impossible. 'No man can go near the sun,' they said. 'It is far too hot and fierce.' Maui answered: 'Have you not seen all the things I have done already? You have seen me change myself into all the birds of the forest, and back again into a man as I am now. I did that by enchantments, and without even the help of the jawbone of my great ancestress, which I now have. Do you really suppose that I could not do what I suggest?'

The brothers were persuaded by these arguments, and agreed to help him. So they all went out collecting flax, and brought it home, and sat there twisting it and plaiting it. And this was when the methods were invented of plaiting flax into tuamaka, or stout, square-shaped ropes, and paharahara, or flat ropes; and the method of twisting the fibre into round ropes. When they had made all the ropes they needed, Maui took up the jawbone of Muri ranga whenua, and away they went, carrying their provisions

The sun came up from his pit

with them, and the ropes. They travelled all that night, having set out at evening lest the sun should see them. When the first light of dawn appeared, they halted and hid themselves so that the sun should not see them. At night they resumed their journey, and at dawn they hid themselves again, and in this way, travelling only when the sun could not observe them, they went far away to the eastward, until they came to the edge of the pit from which the sun rises.

On each side of this place they built a long high wall of clay, with huts made of branches at either end to hide in. There were four huts, one for each of the brothers. When all was ready they set their noose and saw that it was as strong as they could make it. The brothers lay waiting in the huts, and Maui lay hiding in the darkness behind the wall on the western side of the place where the sun rises. He held in his hand the jawbone of his ancestress, and now he gave his brothers their final instructions:

'Mind you keep hidden,' he said. 'Don't go letting him see you or you'll frighten him off. Wait until his head and his shoulders are through the noose. Then when I shout, pull hard, and haul on the ropes as fast as you can. I will go out and knock him on the head, but do not any of you let go your ropes until I tell you. When he's nearly dead we'll let him loose. Whatever you do, don't be silly and feel sorry for him when he screams. Keep the ropes good and tight until I say.'

And so they waited there in the darkness at the place where the sun rises. At length the day dawned, a chilly grey at first, then flaming red. And the sun came up from his pit, suspecting nothing. His fire spread over the mountains, and the sea was all glittering. He was there, the great sun himself, to be seen by the brothers more closely than any man had ever seen him. He rose out of the pit until his head was through the noose, and then his shoulders. Then Maui shouted, and the ropes were pulled, the noose ran taut. The huge and flaming creature struggled and threshed, and leapt this way and that, and the noose jerked up and down and back and forth; but the more the captive struggled, the more tightly it held.

Then out rushed Maui with his enchanted weapon, and beat the sun about the head, and beat his face most cruelly. The sun screamed out, and groaned and shrieked, and Maui struck him savage blows, until the sun was begging him for mercy. The brothers held the ropes tight, as they had been told, and held on for a long time yet. Then at last when Maui gave the signal they let him go, and the ropes came loose, and the sun crept slowly and feebly on his course that day, and has done ever since. Hence the days are longer than they formerly were.

It was during this struggle with the sun that his second name was learned by man. At the height of his agony the sun cried out: 'Why am I treated by you in this way? Do you know what it is you are doing, O you men? Why do you wish to kill Tama nui te ra?'

That was his name, meaning Great Son the Day, which was never known before.

After this feat of laming the sun, Maui and his brothers returned to their house and dwelt there.

It is said that one day Maui was exceedingly thirsty. No doubt this was after his visit to the sun. He asked the tieke, or saddleback, to fetch him a drink, but the bird paid no attention, so he threw it in the water and called another bird, the hihi, or stitch-bird. The hihi also took no notice, so he threw it in the fire and its feathers were singed, which accounts for the colour of that bird. He next tried the totoara, or robin, and when it also disobeyed him he placed a streak of white near its beak as a mark for its incivility. At last the kokako, the crow, complied with his request. It went to the water and filled its ears, and returned to Maui. He drank, and as a reward he pulled kokako's legs to make them long, because it had done as he asked. This is true.

Kokako

4

Before the exploit that is related here, the sea was greater and the land was less. Only Hawaiki, the homeland, was dry for men. Maui, in spite of his timid brothers' fears, pulled up the fish that bears his name. The Maori say that the Fish of Maui is New Zealand.

HOW MAUI FISHED UP LAND

MAUI, in the custom of ancient times, had several different names. At the beginning he was Maui potiki because he was the youngest child. Then he had his given name, Maui tikitiki a Taranga, and later he acquired other names for different sides of his character. According to what he was up to he might be known as Maui nukarau, or Maui-the-trickster; Maui atamai, Maui-the-quick-witted; Maui mohio, Maui-the-knowing; Maui toa, Maui-the-brave; and so on. He was an expert at the game of teka, or dart-throwing, and all the best patterns in the string game of whai, or cat's cradles, were invented by Maui. He was also a great kite-flier, and the story is told of a small boy of another name (but it could only have been Maui) who once came half out of the water and snatched the kite-string of a child on the land. He then slipped back into the sea and continued flying it from under the water until his mother was fetched, for she was the only one who could control him and make him behave at that time.

It was Maui, moreover, who invented the type of eel-trap that prevents the eel from escaping once it is in. After he had slain Tuna roa he constructed a hinaki that had a turned-back entrance with spikes pointing inwards, so that the eels went in for the bait and were trapped. Thus he always caught more eels than all his brothers put together. Again, it was Maui who first put a barb on his spear for catching birds. The spears of his brothers all had smooth points, but Maui secretly attached a barb to his, and took it off again so that his brothers would not know. In the same way also he secretly barbed his fish-hooks and always caught more fish than they. This led to some unpleasantness between them.

The brothers grew tired of all his tricks, and tired of seeing him haul up fish by the kitful when they caught only a few. So they did their best to leave him behind when they went out fishing. One day he assumed the form of a tiwaiwaka, or fantail, the restless, friendly little bird that flits round snapping flies. He flew on to their canoe as they were leaving and perched on the prow. But they saw through this at once and turned back, and refused to go out with Maui on board. They said they had had enough of his enchantments and there would only be trouble if he went with them. This meant that he had to stay at home with his wives and children, with nothing to do, and listen to his wives complaining about the lack of fish to eat.

'Oh, stop it, you women,' he said one day when their grumbling had got on his nerves. 'What are you fussing about? Haven't I done all manner of things by my enchantments? Do you think a simple thing like catching a few fish is beyond me? I'll *go* out fishing, and I'll catch a fish so big that you won't be able to eat it all before it goes bad.' He felt better when he had said this, and went off to a place where women were not allowed, and sat down to make himself a fish-hook. It was an enchanted one, and was pointed with a piece chipped off the jawbone of his great ancestress, Muri ranga whenua. When it was finished he chanted the appropriate incantations over it, and tucked it under his maro, the loin cloth which was all he wore.

Meanwhile, since the weather looked settled, the brothers of Maui were tightening the lashings of the top strakes of their canoe, to be ready for an expedition the following day. So during the night Maui went down and hid himself beneath the flooring slats. The brothers took provisions and made an early start soon after daybreak, and they had paddled some distance from the shore before Maui nukarau crept out of his hiding place.

All four of them felt like turning back at once, but Maui by his enchantments made the sea stretch out between their canoe and the land, and by the time they had turned the canoe round they saw that they were much further out than they had thought. 'You might as well let me stay now; I can do the bailing,' said Maui, picking up the carved wooden bailing scoop that was lying beside the bailing-place of the canoe. The brothers exchanged glances and shrugged their shoulders. There was not much point in objecting, so they resumed their paddling, and when they reached the place where they usually fished, one of them went to put the stone anchor overboard. 'No, no, not yet!' cried Maui. 'Better to go much further out.' Meekly, his brothers paddled on again, all the way to their more distant fishing spot, which they only used when there was no luck at the other one. They were tired out with their paddling, and proposed that they should anchor and put their lines overboard. 'Oh, the fish here may be good enough for you,' said Maui, 'but we'd do much better to go right out, to another place I know. If we go there, all you have to do is put a line over and you'll get a bite. We'll only be there a little while and the canoe will be full of fish.' Maui's brothers were easy to persuade, so on they paddled once more, until the land had sunk from sight behind them. Then at last Maui allowed them to put the anchor out and bait their lines.

It was exactly as he had said it would be. Their lines were hardly over the side before they all caught fish. Twice only they had put their lines out when the canoe was filled with fish. They had so many that it would have been unsafe to catch more, for the canoe was now getting low in the water. So they suggested going back.

'Wait on,' said Maui, 'I haven't tried my line yet.'

'Where did *you* get a hook?' they asked.

'Oh, I have one of my own,' said Maui. So the brothers knew for certain now that there was going to be trouble, as they had feared. They told him to hurry and throw his line over, and one of them started bailing. Because of the weight of the fish they were carrying, water was coming in at the sides.

Maui produced his hook from underneath his maro; a magnificent, flashing hook it was, with a shank made of paua shell that
glistened in the sunlight. Its point was made of the jawbone of his
ancestress, and it was ornamented at the top of the shank with
hair pulled from the tail of a dog. He snooded it to a line that was
lying in the canoe. Boastful Maui behaved as if it were a very
ordinary sort of fish-hook, and flashed it carelessly. Then he asked
his brothers for some bait. But they were sulking, and had no
wish to help him. They said he could not have any of their bait.

*Maui's
fish-hooks*

So Maui atamai doubled his fist and struck his nose a blow, and
smeared the hook with blood, and threw it overboard.

'Be quiet now,' he told his brothers. 'If you hear me talking to
myself don't say a word, or you will make my line break.'

And as he paid out the line he intoned this karakia, that calls on
the north-east and south-east winds:

> Blow gently, whakarua,
> blow gently, mawake,
> my line let it pull straight,
> my line let it pull strong.
> My line it is pulled,
> it has caught,
> it has come.
> The land is gained,

> the land is in the hand,
> the land long waited for,
> the boasting of Maui,
> his great land
> for which he went to sea,
> his boasting, it is caught.
> A spell for the drawing up of the world.

The brothers had no idea what Maui was up to now, as he paid out his line. Down, down it sank, and when it was at the bottom Maui lifted it slightly and it caught on something which at once pulled very hard. Maui pulled also, and hauled in a little of his line. The canoe heeled over, and was shipping water fast. 'Let it go!' cried the frightened brothers, but Maui answered with the words that are now a proverb: 'What Maui has got in his hand he cannot throw away.'

'Let go?' he cried. 'What did I come for but to catch fish?' And he went on hauling in his line, the canoe kept taking water, and his brothers kept bailing frantically, but Maui would not let go.

Now Maui's hook had caught in the barge-boards of the house of Tonganui, who lived at the bottom of that part of the sea and whose name means Great South; for it was far to the south that the brothers had paddled from their home. And Maui knew what it was that he had caught, and while he hauled at his line he was chanting the spell that goes:

> O Tonganui,
> why do you hold so stubbornly there below?
> The power of Muri's jawbone is at work on you,
> you are coming,
> you are caught now,
> you are coming up,
> appear, appear.
> Shake yourself,
> grandson of Tangaroa the little.

The fish came near the surface

The fish came near the surface then, so that Maui's line was slack for a moment, and he shouted to it not to get tangled. But then the fish plunged down again, all the way to the bottom. And Maui had to strain, and haul away again. And at the height of all this excitement his belt worked loose, and his maro fell off and he had to kick it from his feet. He had to do the rest with nothing on.

The brothers of Maui sat trembling in the middle of the canoe, fearing for their lives. For now the water was frothing and heaving, and great hot bubbles were coming up, and steam, and Maui was chanting the incantation called Hiki, which makes heavy weights light.

At length there appeared beside them the gable and thatched roof of the house of Tonganui, and not only the house, but a huge piece of the land attached to it. The brothers wailed, and beat their heads, as they saw that Maui had fished up land, Te Ika a Maui, the Fish of Maui. And there were houses on it, and fires burning, and people going about their daily tasks. Then Maui hitched his line round one of the paddles laid under a pair of thwarts, and picked up his maro, and put it on again.

'Now while I'm away,' he said, 'show some common sense and don't be impatient. Don't eat food until I come back, and whatever you do don't start cutting up the fish until I have found a priest and made an offering to the gods, and completed all the necessary rites. When I get back it will be all right to cut him up, and we'll share him out equally then. What we cannot take with us will keep until we come back for it.'

Maui then returned to their village. But as soon as his back was turned his brothers did the very things that he had told them not to. They began to eat food, which was a sacrilege because no portion had yet been offered to the gods. And they started to scale the fish and cut bits off it. When they did this, Maui had not yet reached the sacred place and the presence of the gods. Had he done so, all the male and female deities would have been appeased by the promise of portions of the fish, and Tangaroa would have been content. As it was they were angry, and they caused the fish of Maui to writhe and lash about like any other fish.

That is the reason why this land, Aotearoa, is now so rough and mountainous and much of it so unuseful to man. Had the brothers done as Maui told them it would have lain smooth and flat, an example to the world of what good land should be. But as soon as the sun rose above the horizon the writhing fish of Maui became solid underfoot, and could not be smoothed out again.

This act of Maui's, that gave our people the land on which we live, was an event next in greatness to the separation of the Sky and Earth.

Afterwards these young men returned to their home in Hawaiki, the homeland. Their father, Makea tutara, was waiting for them when they beached their canoe, singing a chant that praised the mighty fishing feat of Maui. He was delighted with Maui, and said to him in front of the brothers:

'Among all my children only you, Maui tikitiki, are a great hero. You are the renewal of the strength that I once had. But as for your elder brothers here, they will never be famous like you. Stand up, Maui tikitiki, and let your brothers look at you.'

This was all that Makea tutara had to say to Maui on that occasion. Afterwards Maui fetched his mother also, and brought her to Hawaiki, and they all lived together there.

Thus was dry land fished up by Maui, which had lain beneath the sea ever since the great rains that were sent by the Sky father and the god of winds. The Maori people say that the north island of Aotearoa, which certainly is shaped much like a fish, is Te Ika a Maui; and according to some tribes the south island is the canoe from which he caught it. And his hook is the cape at Heretaunga once known as Te matau a Maui, Maui's Fishhook.*

In some of the other islands which lie across the sea towards Hawaiki, the people say that theirs is the land that Maui pulled up from below.

* Cape Kidnappers

*Before the events that are related in this story
Mahuika alone possessed the gift of fire, and all
fire in the world was got from her. After Maui
had tricked her, fire was kept in the wood of
certain trees, from which men were able to
release it.*

HOW MAUI PLAYED WITH FIRE

IN one of his mischievous moods Maui one day felt like putting
out all the fires in the world. He knew that fire could be obtained only from his ancestress Mahuika, goddess of fire, and he
wanted to see what would happen if he extinguished everybody's
fire. During the night, therefore, he got up and went through the
village putting out all the fires that were smouldering in the cooking houses of each family.

Early next morning he called out to his pononga, or servants:
'I'm hungry! I'm hungry! Cook some food for me, quickly.' One
of the servants hurried to obey him, and found the fire out. He ran
to the next house for a light, and went from house to house through
the village. All the fires were out. Soon the whole village was up
and talking about it and discussing what to do.

When Maui's mother heard what had happened she called some
of the servants to her and ordered them to get ready to go to her
great ancestress Mahuika. 'Tell her that fire has been lost on earth,'
she said, 'and ask her to give some to the world again.' But the
servants stood there trembling. Although they had not set eyes on
Mahuika, they had heard about her and the place where she lived,
and had no wish to visit it. No punishment that might await them
in the village would persuade them. The old people, the sacred
chiefs, repeatedly commanded them to go, and they refused.

'Very well,' said Maui, who had been waiting for this, 'I will go.
I will fetch down fire for the world, if you will show me the way.'

'If you will go then,' said his mother, 'you have only to follow that wide path in front of you there. Keep on, and you will reach the home of an ancestress of yours. You will not be able to mistake the place. All fire comes from there. If she asks you who you are, you had better call out your name at once, so that she may know you are a descendant of hers. But be careful, Maui, and don't try playing any of your tricks on *her*. Your father and I have heard about your deeds, and we know you are fond of deceiving and injuring people. If you happen to be thinking of playing some trick on your ancestress Mahuika, take my advice and do nothing of the sort.'

'No, no,' said Maui. 'I only want to bring back fire for the village. I shall come back as soon as I can get it.'

And so he left the village by the path that his mother had shown him, and after journeying, he reached the abode of the goddess of fire. What he saw there filled him with wonder, and for a long time he stood unable to speak. At length he spoke to Mahuika: 'Old ancestress, would you rise up and tell me where your fire is kept? All the fires in our village have gone out, and I have come to beg some from you.'

The old lady rose up to her full height. 'Aue!' she cried. 'Who can this mortal be?' And Maui answered: 'It is I.'

'Where are you from?' Mahuika asked him.

'I have come,' Maui said.

'You do not belong to this country,' said the old woman. 'Your appearance is not like that of the people of this place. Do you come from the north-east?'

He answered, 'No.'

'Do you come from the south-east?'

'No.'

'Are you from the south?'

'No.'

'Are you from the west, then?'

'No.'

'Do you come from whence the wind comes that blows upon me?'

And Maui said, 'I do.'

'Oh then,' she cried, 'you are my grandchild!' She stepped forward and put her face close up to his and asked him: 'What do you want here?'

'I am come to beg some fire of you. All the fires in our village have gone out.'

'Welcome! Welcome, then!' cried the old woman. 'Here is fire for you.' And she pulled out the nail of koiti, her little finger, and gave it to him. As she drew it out, fire flowed from it. Maui marvelled at this, and took the nail, and left her. But he had only gone a short distance when he mischievously put it out. He went back to her and said: 'The light you gave me has gone out. Would you give me another?' So she pulled out the nail of manawa, her third finger, and it became a flame, and she gave it to him. Maui left her, and this nail also he put out when he had gone a little distance. He wetted his hand, to show Mahuika he had fallen into a stream. Then she gave him the nail of mapere, her middle finger, and he did the same again, and Mahuika believed him each time. In this way she gave him the nail of koroa, her forefinger, and then of koro matua, her thumb. And each one of them Maui put out, and returned for more. He wanted to see what would happen if he took from Mahuika the last of her fire, and he now had not a thought for the fire they needed in the village. This went on until Mahuika had pulled out all the nails of her other hand, and then she began on her toes, until Maui had been given all the nails of her hands and all those of her feet except for one big toe.

Then at last the old woman decided that Maui must be playing some trick on her. She drew out the one nail that remained, the nail of her big toe, and fire flowed from it. But instead of handing it to Maui, she dashed it to the ground, and the whole place caught fire.

'There, you have it all now!' she cried. And Maui was already

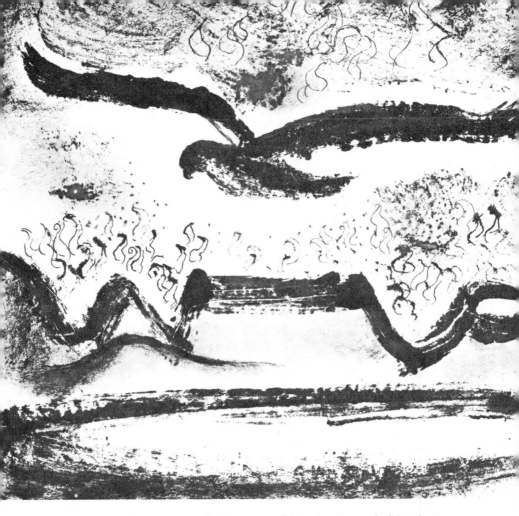

The fire pursued Maui and scorched his feathers

running for his life, with the fire at his heels pursuing him. Looking round, he saw that the whole land would soon be aflame. So he changed himself into a karearea, or hawk, and tried to soar above the flames. But the fire pursued him there and scorched his feathers, which accounts for the colour of that bird. Seeing a lake, he plunged down into it, but found that it was almost boiling. All the forests then caught fire, the land everywhere was alight, and Maui came very near to death.

Then he called on his ancestor Tawhiri matea and all his offspring, to send down rain. 'Let water be given to quench this fire!' he cried, and spoke the appropriate chants. Great clouds appeared, and Tawhiri sent down first the small rain, and then the lasting rain, and everything was drenched, and the flames went out. Even Mahuika herself almost perished before she could reach her place of shelter, and her shrieks were as loud as those of Maui when he was scorched. The waters rose all around her, and in this way Mahuika was deprived of her former power. But fire was saved for the world. When the waters reached her tikitiki, or the topknot of her head, the last seeds of fire fled from it to the rata, the hinau, the kahikatea, the rimu, and certain other trees. These trees would not admit them, and so they went to the mahoe, the totara, the patete, the pukatea, and the kaikomako, where they were cherished. These are the trees from whose dry wood fire can be obtained by friction. The others are of no use for this purpose.

When Maui returned to the village his parents saw his burns and knew what had happened. They said to him: 'We warned you before you went there not to play any of your tricks on Mahuika, and yet you paid no attention. It serves you right that you were nearly burned to death.'

But Maui stood with his hands on his hips and took it lightly. 'Oh! what do I care?' he said. 'Do you think I'm going to be different because of this? Certainly not! I'm going to go on being the same. For *ever*!'

His father answered in a quiet voice: 'Yes, you may please yourself, whether you die or live. If you would only listen to me you would save your life, but if you will not, it will be the worse for you, and that is all I can say.'

After this, Maui went off looking for companions to join him in new adventures.

He did not bring any fire back for the village. From that day forward it was obtained by rubbing a stick of kaikomako, or one of the other trees, in a groove made in another piece of wood.

Before he committed the horrible deed which is related here Maui had performed many feats that brought benefit to man. But out of envy he turned to evil, and was a man who merited punishment.

HOW MAUI'S SISTER LOST HER HUSBAND

MAUI had a sister, whom we have not mentioned before. She was a beautiful, graceful girl, and was called Hinauri. She was married to a fellow called Irawaru, whom Maui did not like. One day Maui and Irawaru went fishing together, and because he did not want his brother-in-law to know about his barbed hooks, Maui took one of the smooth-tipped kind, which were used for catching certain sorts of fish. They paddled out and put their lines over the side, and Irawaru caught plenty of fish, while Maui caught none. This annoyed Maui greatly. He was sitting at his end of the canoe getting angry about it when Irawaru got another bite and at once began to haul his line in. But it had become entangled with Maui's, and when he felt the tugging, Maui thought that *he* had a fish at last. So he began to haul in too, feeling very pleased. In a moment, there were the two men at opposite ends of the canoe hauling in different directions. And soon the fish appeared, flashing about just below the water.

Maui, who was losing his temper, called out rudely: 'Hey! let go my line! He's on *my* hook.' 'No he isn't, he's on mine,' said Irawaru. Maui shouted angrily, 'Come on, let go! He's on *my* line, I tell you.' So Irawaru slacked his line and let Maui pull in the fish. Then Maui saw that Irawaru was right. The fish was on his hook. Irawaru could see it too, and again he asked Maui to let go. 'Can't you wait,' said Maui, 'until I get the hook out?'

He removed Irawaru's hook from the fish's mouth, and found

that it was barbed. His anger boiled over inside him then, to think that all this time, when he could have been using a barbed hook, Irawaru had learned the trick anyway and was catching all the fish. Maui could see that there was no chance of getting even, now. The more they fished the more Irawaru would catch, and Maui would catch nothing. After a few minutes he suggested calmly: 'I think we might as well go back now. What do you think?' Irawaru was all too well aware of Maui's anger. He could feel it from the other end of the canoe. So he was glad to agree, especially since he now had all the fish he wanted. And so they paddled back to the beach.

As they got there a wave threw them slightly to one side and on to some rocks, and they needed to get the outrigger over these in order to get in. Maui, always accustomed to giving orders, said to his brother-in-law: 'Jump out and put your back under the float and lift it, will you?' And Irawaru did so.

As soon as Irawaru was stooping under the weight of the outrigger and was at a disadvantage among the rocks, Maui ran out on the cross-beams and jumped up and down on the outrigger. Irawaru crumpled under it, and Maui practically killed him. If he did not crush him to death he nearly drowned him. When Irawaru was nearly done for, Maui slipped down and trampled on his body, and lengthened his backbone, and by his enchantments drew it out like a tail. And he transformed Irawaru into a dog, and made him eat some nasty filth. Then he began to feel satisfied. This dog was the first of all dogs.

After this, Maui dragged the canoe to the beach and put everything straight, and went home. When he reached the village there was his sister Hinauri, waiting for her husband. She ran up and asked Maui where he was. 'I left him down at the canoe,' said Maui calmly. 'He asked me to tell you to go down and help him carry up the fish. All the ones we caught were his, so you'd better go down. If you don't see him,' Maui said over his shoulder as Hinauri left, 'just call out. And if he doesn't answer, try calling

"Moi, moi! Moi, moi!"—like that.' And he made the sound by which our people call their dogs.

So Hinauri ran down to the canoe, and not seeing Irawaru anywhere about she called his name. Then, remembering what Maui had said, she called out 'Moi, moi! Moi, moi!' Irawaru, who had been snuffling about in the bushes above the beach, recognised her voice then, and came running and barking, 'Ao, ao! ao, ao!' And he frisked and jumped about her, and wagged his tail, and followed her all the way back to the village.

Poor Hinauri, when she realised that her husband had been turned into a dog by Maui, was overcome with grief. It was all she could do to walk to the village. She wept the whole way, and the dog ran around her and waited for her along the track with its tail wagging. She went straight into her house without speaking to anyone, and took an enchanted belt that was hers and put it on, and walked back to the sea by the very path which only a little while before she had run down so gladly. All she wanted was to die, as soon as possible. When she got to the beach she sat down on the rocks for a while and wept, and her tears became part of the waves. And after repeating an incantation that was used by people whose grief made them long for death, she threw herself off the rocks, and the tide swept Hinauri out to sea.

Yet this was not the end of Hinauri.

5

Before the overreaching crime of Maui which is related here, death did not have power over man. Afterwards all men were mortal, and their spirits were gathered in by Hine nui te Po.

HOW MAUI GAVE MORTALITY TO MAN

AFTER what he had done to Irawaru, Maui found it advisable to leave that village and live somewhere else. He went to his parents, in the country of the manapau trees. When he had been there for a time his father decided to have a talk with him.

'My son,' said Makea tutara one evening at dusk, when they were sitting outside the house, 'I have heard from your mother and from others that you are brave and capable, and that in everything you have undertaken in your own country you have succeeded. That says a great deal for you. But I have to warn you: now that you have come to live in your father's country you will find that things are different. I am afraid that here you may meet your downfall at last.'

'What do you mean?' said Maui. 'What things are there here that could be my downfall?'

'There is your great ancestress Hine nui te Po,' said Makea, gravely. And he watched Maui's face as he mentioned the name of Great Hine the Night, the daughter and the wife of Tane and goddess of death. But Maui did not move an eyelid. 'You may see her, if you look,' Makea went on, pointing to where the sun had gone down, 'flashing over there, and opening and closing, as it were.' His thoughts were on death as he spoke. For it was the will of Hine nui, ever since she turned her back on Tane and descended to Rarohenga, that all her descendants in the world of light should follow her down that same path, returning to their mother's womb that they might be mourned and wept for.

'Oh, nonsense,' said Maui affectionately to the old man. 'I don't think about that sort of thing, and you shouldn't either. There's no point in being afraid. We might just as well find out whether we are intended to die, or to live forever.'

Now Maui had not forgotten what his mother once said about Hine nui te Po: that he would some day vanquish her, and death would then have no power over men. He remembered this now, and was not moved by his father's fears.

But Hine nui was the sister of Mahuika, and she knew of Maui's dangerous trickery at the abode of fire, and was resolved to protect her other descendants from further mischief of this kind.

'My child,' said Makea now in a tone of deep sorrow, 'there has been a bad omen for us. When I performed the tohi ceremony over you I missed out a part of the prayers. I remembered it too late. I am afraid this means that you are going to die.'

'What's she like, Hine nui te Po?' asked Maui.

'Look over there,' said Makea, pointing to the ice-cold mountains beneath the flaming clouds of sunset. 'What you see there is Hine nui, flashing where the sky meets the earth. Her body is like a woman's, but the pupils of her eyes are greenstone and her hair is kelp. Her mouth is that of a barracuda, and in the place where men enter her she has sharp teeth of obsidian and greenstone.'

'Do you think she is as fierce as Tama nui te ra, who burns things up by his heat?' asked Maui. 'Did I not make life possible for man by laming him and making him keep his distance? Was it not I who made him feeble with my enchanted weapon? And did the sea not cover much more of the earth until I fished up land with my enchanted hook?'

'All that is very true,' said Makea. 'And you are my last-born son, and the strength of my old age. Very well then, be it as it will. Go there, and visit your ancestress if that is your wish. You will find her there where the earth meets the sky.' And they sat for a while in the dusk, until the red clouds turned to grey and the mountains into black.

Next morning early, Maui went out looking for companions for the expedition. The birds were up when he left, and among them he succeeded in finding several who were willing to go with him. There was tiwaiwaka, the little fantail, flickering about inquisitively and following Maui along the track as if he might have something for him. There was miromiro, the grey warbler, tataeko, the whitehead, and pitoitoi, the robin, who is almost as tame and curious as the fantail.

Maui assembled a party of these friends and told them what he intended to do. They knew that it was an act of great impiety to invade the realm of Hine nui te Po with mischievous intentions. And now, they learned, it was Maui's idea to enter her very body. He proposed to pass through the womb of Great Hine the Night, and come out by her mouth. If he succeeded, death would no longer have the last word with regard to man; or so his mother had told him long ago. This, then, was to be the greatest of all his exploits. Maui, who once had travelled eastward to the very edge of the pit where the sun rose, and southward over the great Ocean of Kiwa to where he fished up land, and all the way to the dwelling-place of Mahuika—Maui now proposed a journey to defy great Hine in the west.

Taking his enchanted weapon, the sacred jawbone of Muri ranga whenua, he twisted its strings around his waist. Then he went into the house and threw off his clothes, and the skin on his hips and thighs was as handsome as the skin of a mackerel, with the tattooed scrolls that had been carved there with the chisel of Uetonga. And off they went, with the birds twittering in their excitement. When they arrived at the place where Hine nui lay asleep with her legs apart and they could see those flints that were set between her thighs, Maui said to his companions:

'Now, my little friends, when you see me crawl into the body of this old chieftainess, whatever you do, do not laugh. When I have passed right through her and am coming out of her mouth, then you can laugh if you want to. But not until then, whatever you do.'

His friends twittered and fluttered about him and flew in his way. 'O sir,' they cried, 'you will be killed if you go in there.'

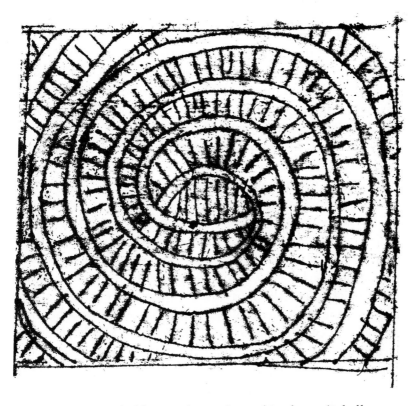

'No,' said Maui, holding up his enchanted jawbone. 'I shall not— unless you spoil it. She is asleep now. If you start laughing as soon as I cross the threshold, you will wake her up, and she will certainly kill me at once. But if you can keep quiet until I am on the point of coming out, I shall live and Hine nui will die, and men will live thereafter for as long as they wish.'

So his friends moved out of his way. 'Go on in then, brave Maui,' they said, 'but do take care of yourself.'

Maui at first assumed the form of a kiore, or rat, to enter the body of Hine. But tataeko, the little whitehead, said he would never succeed in that form. So he took the form of a toke, or earthworm. But tiwaiwaka the fantail, who did not like worms, was against this. So Maui turned himself into a moko huruhuru, a kind of caterpillar that glistens. It was agreed that this looked best, and so Maui started forth, with comical movements. The little birds now did their best to comply with Maui's wish. They sat as still as they could, and held their beaks shut tight, and tried not to laugh. But it was impossible. It was the *way* Maui went in that gave them the giggles, and in a moment little tiwaiwaka the fantail could no longer contain himself. He laughed out loud, with his merry, cheeky note, and danced about with delight, his tail flickering and his beak snapping. Hine nui awoke with a start. She realised what was happening, and in a moment it was all over with Maui. By the way of rebirth he met his end.

Thus died this Maui we have spoken of, who was formed in the topknot of Taranga and cast in the sea, but was saved and nurtured to lead a life of mischief. And thus did the laughter of his companions at the last and most scandalous of his exploits deprive mankind of immortality. For Hine nui always knew what Maui had it in mind to do to her. But she knew that it was best that man should die, and return to the darkness from which he comes, down that path which she made to Rarohenga. Wherefore our people have the saying: 'Death came to the mighty when Maui was strangled by Hine nui te Po, and so it has remained in the world.'

Before he died, Maui had children, and both sons and daughters were born to him in the manner of man and not of the gods. Some of his descendants still live in Hawaiki, the homeland, and some of them came here to Aotearoa, which is the name that was given to the Fish of Maui when it was discovered by the Maori people. These stories that relate the life of Maui were carefully remembered by those descendants and handed down, as a thing to be taught to the generations that come after us.

Here follow those traditions that relate what happened to the sister of Maui and to her descendants, showing how certain great evils came into the affairs of men and wars began between their tribes, but also how the gods protect and help those men who make due offering to them.

HOW HINAURI BECAME THE WIFE OF TINIRAU

WHEN last we heard of Hinauri she was floating out to sea. So deep was her grief at the loss of her husband and the cruelty of her brother that she only wished for death. But Hinauri did not drown. Because of the enchanted girdle she was wearing she floated about for many months until her body was all encrusted with barnacles and seaweed, and in this condition she was washed ashore at a place where she was found by two brothers, whose names were Ihu atamai and Ihu wareware, meaning Handsome-nose and Stupid-nose. They found her lying on the beach and thought she must be dead, but they lifted her up and carried her to their house. They removed the seaweed and barnacles, and when she had been scraped and rinsed they looked on her with pleasure, and for a time she lived as a wife between them both. They inquired her name, but she did not tell them. She made them call her Ihu ngarupaea, or Stranded-nose.

Now these brothers were members of the tribe of Tinirau, a very great chief of those times, who was celebrated for his handsome looks, and for his vanity. Tinirau, who lived on an island named Motutapu, or Sacred Isle, had a number of pools filled with clear water which he used as looking-glasses when he wished to admire himself. He also had a school of small whales, or possibly dolphins, who would answer to his call and perform their lively antics just off shore for his amusement. These were his mokai, or pets, and there was one which he had chosen to be the mokai of his first-born son, when a son should be born to him.

The fame of this chief awoke in Hinauri a strong desire to see him; and word of Hinauri's beauty soon reached Tinirau. For Ihu wareware, or Stupid-nose, went over to Motutapu and told Tinirau all about her—which was typical of Stupid-nose. Hinauri soon grew tired of living with the two brothers, and having heard so much of Tinirau's noble qualities she made up her mind that she would like him for a husband. One day, therefore, when she was out with the women of the village gathering mussels at low tide, she assumed the form of a fish and disappeared. She swam under-water to Motutapu. On the shore of that island she resumed her former shape and sat down to dry her hair. While she was combing it she gave some thought to the best way of meeting Tinirau. Knowing of his great vanity, and of the four pools he used for mirrors, she decided to wait for him at the pools, and to attract attention to herself by splashing about when he came to use them.

On her way along the beach she came to a stranded shark, of the kind whose teeth were prized as ear pendants. 'O fish!' she said, 'you are not the messenger of Tinirau,' and she squatted over it for a moment, and went on her way feeling better. She next saw a stranded whale, and she said and did the same as to the shark. But when she found a repo, or stingray, on the sand, she took off her skirt, which was all she had on, and laid it on the point of the repo. She felt ready then for the meeting with Tinirau, and made her way inland to the pools.

Now Tinirau was so particular about these pools that he had had some wicker fences built around them, and kept a pair of owls whose duty it was to perch in a high tree near his house and let him know if anyone went near them. Their names were Ruru mahara, or Thoughtful-owl, and Ruru wareware, or Stupid-owl.

When Hinauri broke into one of the pools, Thoughtful-owl

'The pools have been destroyed'

flew down to Tinirau and said: 'The pools, the reflecting waters of Tinirau, have been destroyed.'

'No such thing,' said Stupid-owl, who had flown there too. 'Not true!'

So Tinirau ordered them to fly over to the pools and make sure. They returned, and Thoughtful-owl told Tinirau that the enclosures had been knocked down, and there was a man in the water. 'It's all lies,' said Stupid-owl. 'Those words are fiction!'

'You two stay here,' said Tinirau impatiently, and got up. 'I'll go and see for myself.' And he went to the pools, in a very bad mood.

Hinauri saw him coming, and greeted him in a charming fashion. He returned her greeting, and was so surprised that he sat down beside her, in a good mood now.

'When you go out fishing, do you always catch something?' said Hinauri shyly, to make conversation.

'No, I catch nothing,' Tinirau answered untruthfully, while admiring her lovely hair and her soft brown eyes.

'When you pull up your line do you always find your hook and sinker still there?' asked Hinauri, who was watching the mud squeeze up between her toes.

'No,' said Tinirau, who had snapped off a piece of grass and was pulling it, 'I always find my hook and sinker gone.' And he fell in love with Hinauri there and then, and they walked away to a place where they lay down under Tinirau's cloak.

Now Tinirau already had two wives. Their Maori names are rather long but their meanings were The Enraged One and The Jealous One. When these wives heard that Tinirau had met a young woman by the pools and had not since come home, they summoned Thoughtful-owl and Stupid-owl and sent them to find out what was happening. The owls flew off, and came back after a while. 'Well,' said the wives, 'what did you see?'

'We saw two heads and four feet,' said Thoughtful-owl.

'All fiction,' said Stupid-owl. 'Not true!'

Tinirau and Hinauri remained together. One day Tinirau said to her, 'Let us go to my village now, as we shall have food provided for us there.' But Hinauri chanted,

> Let it down, let it down,
> descend, Oh descend,

and sufficient food came down in front of them. They ate it, but they were cold for want of clothing, and when Tinirau said 'Let us go to my place, we'll be frozen here,' she repeated her chant, and clothes came down before them. Meanwhile, Tinirau's other two wives became jealous of Hinauri.

In due course Hinauri went to the village and gave birth to a child, who was the son of Ihu atamai. After that they called her names, and accused her of stealing their husband, and when the baby was a few days old they came to see Hinauri.

'You will need to mind how you behave to your sisters-in-law,' said Tinirau before they arrived, but Hinauri answered: 'If they come in anger it will be evil.'

The two wives came, and Hinauri stood up, holding in her hand the piece of obsidian with which her baby's navel-cord had been cut. One of the wives had a weapon with her. But Hinauri had time to utter a powerful incantation, which called on the god named Whiro, one of the lesser sons of Rangi and Papa, and a killer of men. These were the words:

> Loud sounds the stone,
> sharp pain is the stone,
> to strike at the seat of life is the stone,
> to strike the brain is the stone.
> Behold, the stone rings out,
> behold, the stone will destroy,
> the stone of Whiro te tupua,
> spirit even of thee,
> the man-destroyer.

As she uttered this spell Hinauri threw the piece of obsidian at the two wives, who fell on their backs and died; and their bodies burst open where the stone had struck them, and were seen to be filled with pounamu, or greenstone.

Then Hinauri called out to her husband: 'Look, here are your sinkers that you thought you'd lost!'

In this way pounamu or greenstone was formed, the hard green jade of which the Maori made their most precious ornaments, such as ear pendants, and the tiki that is hung from the neck, and adzes, and even the war club known as mere, when pieces large enough could be obtained.

Then Hinauri had Tinirau to herself for a while, and she lived as the wife of this chief. After some time she went away to visit her relations in her former home, the village of Irawaru, and took with her the little boy. Tinirau found that he missed her very much, and before long he also made his way to that village. As he approached the place he saw some children playing in a swampy place among some toetoe. He hid himself in the toetoe and watched the

Greenstone tiki

children for a while. Then he made a noise like a bird to attract their attention, and when they came to see what it was, he recognised his wife's little boy by the ear pendant he was wearing. It was made of greenstone from one of the wives that were slain. Around his neck Tinirau was wearing a hei, a little scented bag that Hinauri had given him as a love token in their early days together. It was filled with karamea, a perfume made from spear grass. Untying it, he handed it to the boy and told him to take it to his mother. The boy did so, and Hinauri knew at once what it was and who had given it to him. And she came to Tinirau, and took him to the village, where he was received with much honour and ceremony.

For so great a chief as Tinirau there had to be a succession of lavish feasts, and soon it was the same old story: the food stocks of the village were exhausted, and they were down to eating fern roots. To make things worse, their fishing parties were returning empty-handed. No longer was Maui there to catch fish for that village.

One day when Hinauri sat down to eat with her relations they nudged her away and said: 'Your husband does not go to get food.' Hinauri was humiliated, and wept, and Tinirau, seeing this, asked her the reason.

'Go to your brothers,' said Tinirau when she had told him, 'and tell them to cut timber and build a very large whata.' A whata was a platform used for storing food, built to about the height of a man's shoulders, to keep the food away from rats and dogs.

They cut the timber and built the whata, and asked her, 'Where will all the food come from to fill this whata?' She went back to Tinirau.

'Go and tell them to add to it,' said Tinirau, 'and make it larger still.' When this had been done he sent her to fetch two pieces of wood, to make fire by friction. She brought two dead pieces of kaikomako, one of the trees in which the fire of Mahuika took refuge when Maui called for the rains that quenched that goddess. Then he told them at the village that he would arrange a plentiful supply of fish so long as everyone would remain with their doors and windows closed all night. To this they readily agreed, and towards evening Tinirau took the two pieces of wood that Hinauri had fetched, and went to the shore and made a fire, and performed ceremonies and uttered incantations.

Throughout the night a rushing sound was heard, but the people of the village kept their promise; no person opened a door or window all that night. In the morning they found the whata completely covered with fish of every kind. Such a quantity there was that many fishes had slipped off the edges of the whata and lay about on the ground.

Tinirau and Hinauri were able to stay with her relations for some time longer. Then they returned to Motutapu, for she was due to have another child, who was the child of Tinirau. But in the months before this child was born Tinirau began to slight her, and went to live with one of his other wives. This hurt Hinauri very much, but she bore it in silence. As her confinement was approaching, she developed a craving for a particular kind of fish, which Tinirau knew how to catch. So strong was the craving that she had to overcome her pride and send two servants to Tinirau, explaining her need and asking him to catch some of this kind of fish. They addressed him respectfully, saying, 'E Tinirau e!' and he answered, 'E!'

'Your wife is unwell,' they said, and gave him Hinauri's message.

He went to her house in a very bad mood. 'What is the matter with you?' he asked unkindly.

'It is my child,' she said. 'It is about to be born.'

Now Tinirau did not get her the fish she wanted. Instead, he ordered a screen to be built around her sleeping-house of ongaonga, a poisonous nettle, bound up with flax and built so high that she could not possibly get out. The screen was made, and poor Hinauri suffered deeply for the lack of her husband's love at this time. Soon afterwards the child was born. It was a son, and Tinirau now felt pleased, for this was his first-born son. Hearing of it, he went to have the screen of nettles cut away. By this time, though, Hinauri's heart had turned against him. She had cried out in her sorrow to her brother Maui mua. And Maui mua, unknown to her, was just then searching for her with the help of his ancestor Rehua. At that very moment when her need of him was great, he found her and arrived to help and comfort her.

HOW RUPE FOUND HINAURI

THIS is the manner in which Hinauri's brother found her and saved her from Tinirau's unkindness. After the death of Irawaru and the disappearance of Hinauri by the seashore, Maui mua grieved for the loss of his sister. No grief had moved him when his brother Maui tikitiki a Taranga left that village and this world, but when Hinauri disappeared he could think of nothing else, and at length he decided that he must go and find her. He never believed that she was dead. He knew that her enchanted girdle had been missing since the day she disappeared, and he was convinced that it must have saved her.

He visited every island and every village he could think of, yet nowhere could anyone give him news of Hinauri. There was only one thing left to do. He must ascend to the heavens, and consult his great ancestor Rehua, one of the sons of Rangi and Papa, who lived in the topmost of the heavens at a place called Te Putahi nui o Rehua, or the Great Crossroads of Rehua. Neither Maui mua nor any mortal had ever been there before. What Maui mua did not know was that now that his brother was dead, killed in trying to cross the forbidden threshold of Hine nui te Po, the gifts of Maui tikitiki a Taranga had passed to him.

So he went on his way, searching everywhere for a way to reach his ancestor Rehua. At length he came to a place where people were living, it was the first of the heavens, and he asked them: 'Are the heavens above this place inhabited?' They replied: 'They are inhabited,' and he asked them, 'Can I reach those heavens?' The people answered: 'You cannot reach them, the heavens above these are those whose boundaries were fixed by Tane.'

But Maui mua forced a way up through those heavens, and found another place where people were living. He asked these people in the same way, 'Are the heavens above these inhabited?' and they replied, 'They are inhabited.' He asked again, 'Do you think I can reach them?' and they answered 'No, you will not be able to reach them. Those heavens and their boundaries were fixed there by Tane.'

But Maui mua forced a way up through those heavens as well, and so he went on until he reached the heaven which is beyond the ninth, and there he found the abode of Rehua. When Rehua saw a stranger approaching he went to him and gave the customary welcome, weeping and lamenting over him; for it was the custom of our people to weep when friends arrived, not when they departed. Rehua did this without knowing who the stranger was, but Maui mua in his answering lamentation made use of prayers that enabled Rehua to guess in secret who he was.

When their lamentations of welcome were over, Rehua ordered his servants to light fires and prepare food for the visitor. The fires were soon burning, and many gourds were brought and laid before Rehua, but they were empty. Maui mua wondered where the food was to come from that would fill these gourds. Then he noticed that Rehua was loosening the binding of his topknot, on the sacred part of his head. When Rehua's hair was loose the old man shook his head, and out flew flocks of tuis, shining black, with their neat white bibs at their throats. They had been nesting there and feeding on Rehua's head-lice. As they flew out the servants caught them, and very soon they were plucked and cooked, and all the gourds were filled with huahua, or birds preserved in their own fat. When all was ready the potted birds were laid on the ground in front of the visitor as a gift to him; then they were placed beside him, and Rehua invited him to eat. But Maui mua was so filled with awe in the presence of Rehua, and because of what he had just seen, that he felt quite unable to eat. 'No,' he said, 'I cannot eat this food. I saw these birds let loose from your own hair. Who would dare to eat birds that have fed upon insects on the sacred head of Rehua?' So the gourds remained untouched beside him.

At last Maui mua found courage to ask his ancestor the question he had come so far to put. 'O Rehua,' he said, after coughing softly and clearing his throat to show his diffidence, 'has by any

The tuis flew out of Rehua's hair

chance a confused murmur of voices reached you from the world below, on any subject in which I am interested?' He spoke in this roundabout way, since in Maori custom it was unlucky to mention the name of the thing that is sought, lest it elude the seeker.

'Yes,' said Rehua, for he knew precisely what Maui mua meant, 'Such a murmuring of distant voices has reached me from the island of Motutapu, in the world below these heavens.'

6

These words told Maui mua all that he wished to know. He took his leave of Rehua and, by means of enchantments which he did not know he could command till then, he turned himself into a pigeon, and took flight downwards to the island of Motutapu. From this moment he ceased to be known as Maui mua. His name was Rupe, which is another name for the wood pigeon.

On he flew, on and on, until he could see the island of Motutapu. At first it was nothing more than the shadow of a cloud upon the distant, sparkling sea, but soon it took shape, and he could see its beaches. And he came to the village of Tinirau, and circling round he saw the wall of ongaonga that hemmed in the house of Hinauri. It was at this moment that Hinauri, despairing of any kindness now from Tinirau, called out in her heart for her brother. 'O Rupe,' she cried, 'come to help me now! Tinirau does not love me any longer, my child is born, and I have need of you.'

Rupe fluttered down and settled on the ridgepole of his sister's house. Some people of the village saw him there, and one of them ran to fetch a bird spear, and threw it. But Rupe turned it aside with his beak, and it broke against the ridgepole. When this happened Hinauri knew that this was no ordinary pigeon, and she called out to the people who were trying to catch it: 'Leave the bird alone a moment while I look at it.' Then she looked more closely at the pigeon and asked it why it had come. It opened and shut its beak as if it wished to speak. 'It is my brother Rupe!' cried Hinauri, and began to weep for joy. Then Rupe stood beside his sister as her brother, and spoke this form of greeting, which is known as Toetoetu:

> Hinauri:
> Hinauri is my sister,
> and Rupe is her brother,
> but how came he here?
> Did he come from below?
> Did he come from above?

> Climb up your way,
>> let your love turn to Motutapu.

As soon as Rupe had finished his lamentation of greeting to his sister she began hers, answering:

> Rupe:
> Rupe is my brother,
> and Hinauri is his sister,
> but how came he here?
> Did he come from below?
> Did he come from above?
> Let his path now be upwards, to Rehua.

It was while they were saying their greetings that Tinirau had the wall of nettles opened, and came in to see the baby, his new son. But at that moment when Hinauri said 'Let his path now be upwards, to Rehua', Rupe caught her up with the child, and they flew off together, toward the heavens.

Tinirau, astonished to find that a man had been inside that hedge, called out to Rupe: 'Bring her back! Bring back Hinauri and the child.' Hinauri said: 'Do not consent. But let him have his child.' For Hinauri, in spite of Tinirau's unkindness to her, could not bring herself to deprive him of his son. And so they let the baby gently fall, and Tinirau caught it, and fed it with water, and gave it the name Tuhuruhuru, or Feathery Tu, after the plumage of Rupe and also after the god whose name was Tu, who was the god of fighting.

As Rupe and Hinauri flew over the sea Hinauri also let fall the placenta that had nourished Tuhuruhuru before he was born. It fell into the sea, and was devoured by a shark, and this is the origin of the multitude of large eggs that are found inside the body of a female shark.

At length the brother and the sister reached Rehua's dwelling in Rangi tuarea, the heavens beyond the ninth, and they lived there for a time. And as a kindness in return for Rehua's help to them, Rupe cleaned up the old man's marae, or courtyard, for him. It was in a filthy and unhygienic state, due to the laziness of Rehua's people, and the sight of it disgusted Rupe, which led to a saying of his that became a well known proverb: 'O Rehua,' he said, 'your people are so lazy, if every bit of filth was a lizard I doubt if they would bother to touch its tail to make it run.'

So Rupe made two wooden spades, one called Tahitahia, or Sweep-away, and the other Rakerakea, or Scratch-away, and set to work to tidy up. Then he built a proper turuma to keep the village sanitary. In Maori fashion he built it at the edge of a cliff that was part of that heaven, with a rail for squatting on and a post to hold on to. But he fixed this post too loosely—some say deliberately—so that Rehua, in consequence, lost his son Kaitangata. For when Kaitangata was squatting with his feet on the rail the post came loose, he overbalanced, and fell backwards over that cliff. And his blood ran over the heavens, which is the reason why men now say of a ruddy sky, 'Kaitangata stains the heavens with his blood.'

Now Hinauri could not forget the baby she had left behind, whose very name she did not know. She felt ashamed and suffered from remorse for having abandoned her child, and having left it to Tinirau. After a time, Rupe and Hinauri left the abode of Rehua and returned to their own village.

They let the baby gently fall

pleased. 'Oh,' she said, 'he's just what I want! He'll do to carry water for Rupe.' Before very long Tuhuruhuru was given a gourd and sent to fetch water for Rupe. He brought it, and Rupe held out his hands, but Tuhuruhuru poured it up his nose. Spluttering and cursing, Rupe leapt up crying, 'This brat poured the water up my nose!' and he ran after Tuhuruhuru, and gave him a beating, whereon Tuhuruhuru cried, and said:

> In vain have I come!
> Rupe is my uncle,
> Hinauri is my mother,
> and Tinirau is my father.
> In vain have I come!

But Rupe, still spluttering, did not hear this. 'The little brat is grizzling and crying now, but he asked for it,' he said as he walked away, snorting and trying to clear his nose and the back of his mouth.

That evening there was dancing in the meeting-house, and Hinauri and the other young women stood up to dance. Where-upon Tuhuruhuru, remembering what Tinirau had told him, softly chanted the spell to make a skirt fall down:

> Te tu o Hinauri
> makere, makere.
> Te taupaki o Hinauri
> makere, makere.

No one heard him saying it. And Hinauri, whose skirt at that moment had worked loose while she was dancing, had to stop and hitch it up. She rejoined the dance, and Tuhuruhuru did his chant once more, but this time he was overheard by one of the girls. 'That small boy over there has been making fun of your skirt,' she whispered in Hinauri's ear. So Hinauri ran after Tuhuruhuru, and *she* slapped him, and he cried again, and cried out through his sobs:

In vain have I come!
Rupe is my uncle,
Hinauri is my mother,
and Tinirau is my father.
In vain have I come!

He ran out of the meeting-house very upset, and crying miserably. This touched Hinauri's heart, and suddenly she realised the meaning of the words she had just heard. She called out, 'Come back to me,' and Tuhuruhuru knew then that she had realised who he was. So he ran for all he was worth to the water, to rinse off the ashes that marked him as a slave. Hinauri could not catch up with him, so she called for Rupe to help. 'O Rupe,' she said when he came, 'fly down at once and catch that little boy—he is my son.' Rupe flew immediately to the water, and brought Tuhuruhuru back to the meeting-house. Then there was a great reunion, with everyone looking on. Hinauri wept over Tuhuruhuru, and threw her arms about him and wished she had never let him go in the first place. She was overjoyed to see him for the first time since the day he was born, and to be rid of the bad feelings she had about him. After she had finished her lamentation Hinauri asked him: 'What message have you brought me from your father?'

'He said that you and I and Rupe must all go back for my naming ceremony,' Tuhuruhuru told her. Now this ceremony, known as the purenga, was a very important ritual in the life of any boy, but especially for the son of a chief, and Hinauri was glad that it had not been done yet, and glad that Tinirau wanted her to go; and so was Rupe. In the morning, therefore, after they had made their preparations, the three set off for the village of Tinirau. And Tinirau, who also regretted his past unkindness, was delighted to see them. After they had slept off the fatigue of their journey, he sent messengers in all directions to summon his neighbouring chiefs to attend the purenga of his child.

HOW KAE STOLE TUTUNUI

IN order that Tuhuruhuru should grow up strong and brave and enjoy good fortune, Tinirau decided that his naming ceremony must be carried out by the best tohunga he could find. His choice fell upon Kae, a chief himself in the Ati Hapai tribe, a tohunga tauira of great repute, skilled in performing all the necessary incantations and rituals, and a man of high prestige. So a canoe was sent to Kae's island with the invitation, and in due course he arrived at Tinirau's with all the other guests, and was treated with great deference.

On the day fixed for the ceremony all the fine dress cloaks that Tinirau possessed were spread out in the porch of his house, and clubs of greenstone and whale bone were placed on them, to make a show of wealth and power. Many rolls of newly woven mats and other gifts were laid out ready for the guests, who gathered before them and greeted Tinirau with ceremonial weeping.

Then Kae took up his position and recited all the proper chants, full of learned references to Tane and Tu and the ancestors of man. And he committed the child, as his name declares, to the protection of Tu, the war god. When Kae had finished the ceremonies, all the people moved forward and greeted young Tuhuruhuru with lamentations, and some of them made speeches of welcome to him. Then, when everything had been rightly concluded, the guests were taken to the feast which the women had been preparing. Abundance of tui and pigeons had been grilled and potted, also there were delicious roasted rats. Quantities of fish and eels, pipi and mussels, crayfish and sea-eggs were served as well, and a great many kumara and yams had been cooked in the earth-ovens, and now all was laid before the guests in kono, or little individual baskets of fresh green flax. And Tinirau, since he was pleased with the artistic manner in which Kae had performed the purenga of his son, decided to give the old man a special treat. He went down to the shore and summoned Tutunui, the whale that he had chosen to be Tuhuruhuru's pet. Tutunui came and lay on the beach as he was bidden, and Tinirau sliced a piece off his side, and had it cooked for Kae, who found it delicious, and only wished that there was more.

The feast being over, most of the guests departed for their homes. But Kae, on some excuse, remained a while. When at length he decided it was time to return to his own village—which was known by the name of its great carved meeting-house, Te Tihi o Manono—Tinirau ordered his best canoe to be got ready for him, with a crew of his strongest paddlers. But Kae made some objection to that canoe, and said he would prefer not to go in it. It was all a trick on his part. What he wanted was to persuade Tinirau to let him ride home on the back of Tutunui; for he had it in mind to taste some more of the flesh of that great animal.

Now Tinirau did not like to let Tutunui go out of his sight, and especially in the care of Kae; and he hedged about, and said neither yes nor no. In the end, after Kae had given his most solemn promise to treat the animal well, he gave in. 'Very well.' he said. 'You may borrow the mokai of Tuhuruhuru. But be most particular about this: if you wish to *do* anything on the way, do it on the left side, and not on the right. And when you reach the shore of your island and his belly touches the bottom, he will shake himself to let you know. Then you must jump off at once, on the right-hand side, and wade ashore. He will find his own way back.'

Now during the crossing, Kae disobeyed what Tinirau had said. He did it on the wrong side. And when they reached the shore of Haruru atea and Tutunui's belly scraped the bottom, Tutunui shook himself as Tinirau had said, but Kae did not jump off. He stayed there, and held on tight, pronouncing magic spells that made it impossible for Tutunui to get away. And in his struggles Tutunui got his blowhole blocked with sand, and he died.

Kae went up to fetch his people and they dragged the body ashore, and sliced it up, and feasted on the delicious flesh of Tuhuruhuru's pet. They cooked the meat in earth-ovens, covering it with the fragrant leaves of koromiko before they put the earth on top. And the fat of Tutunui went into the koromiko leaves, which to this day feel greasy to the fingers; and hence the saying, when koromiko leaves are placed on cooking food: 'There's some of the savour of Tutunui.'

Tinirau kept waiting for Tutunui to come home. The night passed after he had left with Kae, and the morning also, and still there was no sign of him. That afternoon the tonga, or south-east wind, sprang up, and on it came to Tinirau's nostrils the savoury smell of Tutunui's roasted flesh. He knew then what Kae had done. His heart grew dark, and he began to plan how he would get his utu, or payment. After some thought he decided that his wife and other women of his village must go to Haruru atea and bring Kae back with them. If men were to go, the Ati Hapai would know at once that war was meant, but a party of women, they would not suspect.

'But how shall we know Kae?' the women asked. For they had been excluded from the priestly ceremonies, and during the feast they had all been busy with the food, and had not seen Kae at close quarters.

'You will recognise him by his teeth,' said Tinirau. 'He has teeth that are all uneven, and overlap one another.'

'But how are we to see his teeth?' the women asked. 'If he keeps his mouth closed all the time, what then?' For in Maori custom it was exceedingly impolite for strangers to ask the name of any chief, who was supposed by his fame and greatness to be known to everyone.

'You'll have to play some silly game,' was Tinirau's reply, 'and make him laugh.'

Away the ladies paddled

That afternoon a large canoe belonging to one of Tinirau's wives was dragged down to the sea, its lashings were tightened, and it was fitted out for the crossing to the land of Kae. Then all the women embarked in it, amongst them Hinauri, and Raukatauri, Raukatamea, Rekareka, and other distinguished women of that time whose names have not been remembered.

Away the ladies paddled, and at evening they reached Kae's village and its famous meeting-house that was renowned for its splendid carvings, the work of generations of master carvers, and for the excellence of its rafter paintings and tukutuku panels. They were received in a friendly manner, and taken into the meeting-house and given the place of honour near the window. The old tohunga was sitting at the foot of one of the centre posts supporting the roof, and mats were laid there for him to recline on; but the visitors did not know yet which was he, out of the many people assembled in the house.

According to custom, they were invited to join in the amuse-ments of their hosts: in waiata, or songs; in whai, or string games; and haka, a chant and dance combined. They gave some items of their own, and some of their songs made the whole gathering rock with laughter—but never the old man beside the post. By this time the women felt sure that this was Kae, but not a single one of their items drew a laugh or even a smile from the dour old man. It seemed as if the crafty Kae knew just what they were watching for.

There was a break in the programme, and on pretence of pre-paring items for the next half the party from Tinirau's held a consultation together. 'Shall we try the Waitoremi?' said one of them. This was a silly song that had whistling in it, quickly alter-nated with the words, and some complicated play with the fingers—very difficult to do and keep a straight face, and difficult to watch without laughing, too. So when the programme was resumed and the visitors were invited to perform again, they did the Waitoremi:

> I teach how to whistle
> and he doesn't whistle,
> I teach how to open out the fingers
> and he doesn't open his.
> Nuku whistles, Rangi whistles!
> Whistle a tune, O Puapua—
> you in the red cloak!
> Whistle a tune, obey my spell!

This song was Kae's undoing. He could not help laughing, and the visitors saw his peculiar teeth, even while they concentrated on their song. From this comes a little custom of the Maori, when someone listening to a story is amused by it and laughs, one nudges one's neighbour and says: 'There's Kae laughing.'

Soon after this the visitors said they were tired from their paddling and their evening's exertions, and asked the Ati Hapai to let their fires burn low so that they could sleep; their real object being, of course, to be able to perform their enchantments over Kae without being seen. But that old tohunga, who suspected something, took two round pieces of paua shell, which had been cut and polished to be put in a carving for eyes, and he put one over each of his eyelids as he lay down to sleep, so that they glinted faintly in the firelight. In this way he hoped to make the visitors think that he was still awake.

The women from Tinirau's, taking no notice, went on with their incantations in the darkness, and whispered this rotu, which has been used so many times since then, to bring sleep on:

> O eyes that see,
> be you closed in sleep,
> be you tightly sealed in sleep, in sleep,
> O eyes that see.

Very soon their rotu had put the whole house into a deep sleep. Not one of Kae's people was awake, and certainly not old Kae, for all that his eyes still seemed to shine. Then the visitors silently got up and formed a line, to carry Kae out of the house. Two of them gently picked up the old tohunga in his sleeping mat with the glinting paua shells still over his eyes, and taking care to cover him with his cloaks and keep him warm, they passed him quietly along the line, and in this way down to their canoe, where two women were standing ready to receive him. And so they laid him, still fast asleep, in their canoe, and paddled away into the night, and shortened the journey by means of certain karakia. Before it was dawn they had laid Kae down beside another housepost—in the house of Tinirau. And there he slept off the effects of their rotu, and at length the shells fell off his eyes, but he still slept on.

Tinirau was delighted, and gave the women all the praise that they deserved. He then ordered that when he emerged in the morning from his own sleeping-house, everyone should call out, 'Here comes Tinirau, here comes Tinirau,' so as to make Kae think he was waking up at home and Tinirau was arriving as a visitor.

And this was done. When it was broad daylight, the cry went up: 'Here comes Tinirau.' Kae stirred out of his enchanted sleep, all drowsy and confused. He thought he was at home, beside one of the posts of Te Tihi o Manono, and Tinirau had come to ask him about Tutunui.

Tinirau came to the door, and paused there. 'Greetings to you, O Kae,' he said. 'How came you here?' Kae grunted something, and sat up a little, saying, 'What do you mean, How came I here? How did *you* come, you mean.'

And Tinirau grinned at the sleepy old man who had killed and eaten the pet of Tuhuruhuru, and asked him: 'How many rafters in your house, Kae?'

Kae looked upwards. He had only to look, he had no need to count. The rafter-paintings were not those of Te Tihi o Manono. He knew that his hour had come, and bowed down his head to his sleeping-mat, and Tinirau's men came in and carried him away. Later he was cooked upon an umu, or earth-oven, and eaten by his enemies; and this was the first time that men had eaten the flesh of men. Thus perished Kae. And this act of revenge of Tinirau's led to interminable wars. Thus wars began between the tribes of men. This is true.

HOW WHAKATAU
DESTROYED THE ATI HAPAI

WHEN Tuhuruhuru grew to manhood he took a wife, whose name was Apakura, and this story is about three of their children: Tuwhakararo, their first-born son; Mairatea, one of their daughters; and Whakatau potiki, their last-born son. All these children grew up on Motutapu, but when the time came for Mairatea to marry she went away. She became the wife of one of the sons of a chief named Poporokewa.

Now Poporokewa was the head of the Ati Hapai tribe—the tribe of Kae. The quarrel with those people, that began when Kae stole Tutunui, was too recent to have been forgotten, but after the death of Tuhuruhuru it was patched up sufficiently for a daughter of his to marry a son of Poporokewa.

After some time Tuwhakararo longed to see his sister, and went to visit her. It was thus that this grandson of Tinirau found himself in the notorious meeting-house, Te Tihi o Manono. Even though there were some among the old people there who had once eaten the delicious flesh of Tutunui, yet he sat in that house with them.

Now one of the daughters of Poporokewa, a beautiful girl named Maurea, took a great fancy to the visitor. Even though she was carrying on a courtship at the time with a young man of her own tribe, who was very anxious to marry a daughter of his chief, Maurea now became interested in Tuwhakararo. This circumstance led to a renewal of the quarrel between these tribes, and to a very great act of utu, or avenging.

One day when games were being held on the marae before Te Tihi o Manono, Tuwhakararo was invited to wrestle with some of the young men of the Ati Hapai. He agreed. But one of his

7

opponents was the jilted lover of Maurea. This young man was glad of the chance to fight his rival, and was determined to injure him, but he proved no match for Tuwhakararo, who quickly gave him some heavy falls. While the crowd all laughed he sat in the dust and sulked, and Tuwhakararo began to dress again. He was just putting his head through the hole in his tupuni, a cloak made like a poncho, when his defeated rival leapt up in hatred and threw sand and dust in his eyes. Tuwhakararo, wild with pain and hampered by his tupuni, tried to rub his eyes; and the young man struck him on the head and killed him. The Ati Hapai, in a mood for sport, were delighted to see the tables turned so suddenly. They rushed in screaming and laughing, and seized Tuwhakararo's body and, remembering now what had been done to Kae, their chiefs had it cooked, and they ate his flesh.

Then they scraped his bones and hung them up in a basket beneath the ridgepole of Te Tihi o Manono. Thus was Kae avenged and Mairatea plunged in grief. For there in the meeting house of her husband's tribe she heard the bones of her own brother rattling in their basket. They seemed to be saying, 'Tauparoro, tauparoro,' (the name for playing mapara, or castanets), and Mairatea answered them: 'You rattle in vain, O bones of him who was devoured by the Ati Hapai. For who is there to take utu for him?'

The fact is, Tuwhakararo had died before having any sons who might avenge him. In due course news of his fate reached Apakura on Motutapu. And when she heard it she decided to call upon Whakatau potiki, her last-born son, to do what was necessary. She went to his place at Paparahi and sang him the chant that was used in such cases. And she said to him, 'I have come to fetch you to avenge the death of your eldest brother, because you are both my children.'

Whakatau agreed at once, and told his mother to return and begin providing for the expedition. 'Make me a canoe,' he said, 'a long spade, and a taiaha also. Let plenty of fern-root be baked for the journey, and prepare a parting feast for the men who will come with me. Let there be plenty of dried shark and roasted birds. Let all the shark oil be kept aside, and put into gourds. I shall have a use for it. As for yourself, do not go to the feast, but wear feathers of mourning and remain indoors.'

These things were done, to the accompaniment of laments that were sung by the women to stir up the feelings of the warriors. A war canoe was built. A heavy ko, or wooden spade, was shaped

Taiaha

for Whakatau, and incantations were said over it to make it sure in its work. A taiaha also, a sort of club-like spear, was made of kahikatoa, or red manuka, and finely carved, and provided with a ruff of red parrot feathers behind the tongue. This taiaha also was rendered tapu by the singing of chants. And the shark oil was poured into several calabashes, as Whakatau had asked.

When Whakatau arrived his new canoe was ready, and so were many hundreds of men who were eager to accompany him, and their canoes were ready for sea also. This, Whakatau did not want. He only wanted to take a small, picked band of men with him.

However, he decided to face this difficulty later. He let them all take part in the rite of whakangau paepae, that prepared for battle. Each man in turn knelt down and bit the crossbar of their turuma, the village latrine, to the saying of protective chants. This done, they all put out to sea, watched by Apakura and the other women of Motutapu.

At an island which they had to pass on the way, Whakatau made everyone go ashore to hold manoeuvres and exercises. They formed up in battle array with spears and clubs, and practised their war dances. Then, with fierce yells, they attacked an imaginary foe. Not being entirely satisfied, Whakatau made the various canoe parties rush a creek and try to jump over it, and some of them failed to make the leap in good order. But his own crew, his handpicked men, sprang over it easily without breaking up.

Now in view of all that they had done, and of their eagerness to fight for him, Whakatau did not wish to offend or disappoint the men. On the other hand, he was determined to take none but the finest fighters with him. He therefore addressed them, saying: 'Listen, all of you. We will not go on until tonight, in case the Ati Hapai should see us coming. We want to surprise them if we can. We will leave here after dark.' And that evening, when the men were sitting round their fires waiting for the order to move, Whakatau sent some of his own party to remove the draining plugs from all the canoes except his own. They did so, and then he gave the order, and in the middle of the night they all embarked, with a great deal of noise and excitement.

As they left that island, the crews began singing in a certain order the rowing chants that had been allotted to them so that they should keep in touch across the water. But presently one canoe began to go down, and then another, and paddlers had to bail. One by one they fell behind, their chanting grew fainter and ceased, and they had to put back to land. Only Whakatau's canoe went on. The name of that canoe was Hikutoto, the word for an expedition of revenge. In it were the gourds of shark oil for which Whakatau had asked his mother.

Because of their late start the night before, Hikutoto did not reach the shores of Haruru atea before daybreak. When the sun came up Whakatau found that he was within sight of Poporokewa's land, and knew that he had probably been seen already. He therefore threw out his anchor-stone at a distance from the shore and waited to see what would happen.

Now the Ati Hapai were a very insulting people, and in their village when this great war canoe had been sighted, everyone went round shouting 'Kumete! Kumete!'—'Bowl of food! Bowl of food!' Crowds of them went down to the beach, and in the front three men who were all named Mango, or Shark. There was Mango urunui, or 'Shark-with-Big-Head'; Mango ururoa, or 'Shark-with-Long-Head'; and Mango urutapena, or 'Shark-with-Insulting-Head'.

The first of these called out across the surf: 'Were you fools enough to come here of your own accord?' The leader of the strangers in the kumete called back, 'Which of the arts of war are you any good at?' 'I am a faster swimmer than any of you weaklings,' Shark-with-Big-Head answered. 'Swim here then, if you dare,' cried Whakatau, and Mango plunged in and swam to the bowl to pull it in. But Whakatau speared him with his ko. So the boaster was killed, and his body was hauled into the kumete. And that was a very disgusting insult, to degrade a man by making him common, like food.

There were shouts of anger from the shore, and mutterings were heard: 'It is the fault of the swimming. Let me swim to the prow direct.' This was the first time that proverb was heard. Then Shark-with-Long-Head shouted insults to the men in the kumete.

'And which of the arts of war are *you* good at?' cried Whakatau. 'None of you fools can beat me at diving,' Mango shouted back. 'Then dive here, if you dare,' cried Whakatau. And Mango dived

On Motutapu, Apakura was sitting on the roof of her house. It was raining lightly, and when she saw the whole sky red with flames she knew that utu had been taken for her first-born son and the Tihi o Manono was destroyed.

This is the end of these stories of Maui and his brothers, of his sister Hinauri and her descendants in the tribe of Tinirau, which show how mischief and evil, and revenge, and the eating of men's flesh, began among our people in ancient times.

Apakura was sitting on the roof of her house

*Tawhaki at one time lived on the earth and had
the appearance of a man. He went one day to the
top of a high hill and, taking off his earthly garments, clothed himself in lightning. Some men
who were cutting brushwood saw this. They told
their people, and from that time he was recognised as a deity, and prayers and chants were
said to him.*

TAWHAKI DESTROYS
THE PONATURI

MANGO and some other cousins of Tawhaki who were
jealous of him attacked him by the side of a pool and left
him for dead. The cousins were jealous because all the young
women of that place admired Tawhaki and would not accept them
as husbands. They were not handsome, and Tawhaki was a splendid chief, most beautiful in his person. The women showed their
preference by inviting him to their house, spreading their finest
mats on the floor for him to lie on, and entertaining him with their
kindest services. One day Tawhaki went to the pool called Rangituhi to wash his head and comb his hair in the reflecting water.
He was chanting this karakia while he washed:

> Spring up, faint light of dawn.
> Give my comb to me,
> the scratcher for my head.
> I will go to the water,
> to the pool Rangituhi,
> yes, to the pool Rangituhi.
> My act is complete.

When Mango and the others saw him there they beat him up

Tawhaki looking at himself in wa

and left him insensible, with grievous wounds. Then they returned to their homes, and Muri whaka roto, the mother of some of those cousins, asked them where Tawhaki was. 'He is still at the pool, washing and combing his hair,' they said.

She waited some time, and as Tawhaki did not return she went outside and called to him, thus: 'Tawhaki, E!' She was answered by the pukeko, a swamp-hen which has blue feathers in its wing and a bright red beak. Pukeko answered 'Ke?' and she went in that direction. Not finding Tawhaki she called again, and this time was answered by the moho, another kind of rail. Moho gave his cry of 'Hu!', and Muri returned to the village. She accused Mango and the others of doing harm to Tawhaki.

'Did he not answer your call?' they asked.

'A pukeko and a moho answered me,' she said. And then she added: 'Tawhaki is not dead, he has gone away to say karakia that will close his wounds. He will recover, and live.'

What Muri said was true. The cool water revived Tawhaki, and when he had come to, he went away a little distance and said this chant:

> It grows in the hair of your head,
> and on your brow the blood glows red—
> the blood, the blood of Tawhaki,
> and of the sun and moon,
> and of the auspicious sky—
> of the sky now above.

Tawhaki then left that place with his younger brother Karihi and went on a long journey. Their purpose was to take utu for the murder of their father, Hema.

These brothers arrived at the place called The Hill of Resting, the home of their sister Pupu mai nono. She asked them: 'Where are you going, my brothers?'

They answered: 'We have come.'

They then went down to the sea to continue their journey, and carelessly walked into the water without saying the incantations necessary for walking on its surface. They only waded deeper and deeper, and had to return to their sister's house.

'You had better stay here tonight,' she said. 'Tomorrow I will see you safely on your way.'

In the morning they set out for the sea again, and Pupu asked them: 'How did the seaweed appear when you were here?'

'When we came yesterday it looked just as it looks now,' said Tawhaki.

'That is why you could not go on,' their sister said. 'Let the time be propitious; then you may go on to your destination.' So they waited until this was the case, and Tawhaki then said the proper karakia for crossing the water, and Pupu said to him: 'Go, but do not let your feet tread in the hollows. Step on the tops of the waves.'

And so they crossed safely, and Tawhaki took to wife Hine tua tai, or Daughter of the Seashore, and begat Ika nui, Great Fish. He also had numerous other wives as they crossed the sea.

On this journey Tawhaki saw a woman whose name was Crooked Fingernails. She was bathing in a pool, and winding her hair into knobs on the top of her head. He also saw Tuna roa, the great eel that was slain by Maui, and from him he learned many incantations that were of help to him in other circumstances. Having learned them he went on, and met two women who were known as Talk of Procreating and Talk of Fertility, because they talked of nothing else. Tawhaki spoke to these two women of other matters, but they did not answer a word. Presently he saw a house in the distance, and met a man named Root-of-all-things.

'Friend,' said Tawhaki, 'what is that house over there?'

'Understand, O young man,' said Root-of-all-things. 'That is the house of the Ponaturi. The bones of Hema are hung up in that house.'

Then Tawhaki and Karihi knew that they had reached the house of the people who had murdered their father.

two taurekareka, or slaves. When they had gone some distance Tawhaki warned the slaves: 'We shall soon pass by the pa of Tongameha. When we do so, be careful not to look up at it, or you two, being unconsecrated persons, will die.' They came to that fort, and one of the servants did look up at it. Instantly, by the enchantments of Tongameha, one of his eyes was plucked out. This caused the death of that slave, and Tawhaki and Karihi went on their way with only one slave.

In due course they reached the dwelling of Tawhaki's great-great-grandmother, Whaitiri, who was matakerepo, or quite blind. She was sitting on the ground counting taro, picking them from a pile on the one hand and putting them on the ground on the other. When she had counted from one to nine, Tawhaki took the tenth away. She counted them again, and this time Tawhaki took the ninth away. She counted them once more, and still there were only eight. As she could not find the two that were missing she stood up, and taking her patu, or club of sperm-whale bone, which she always sat on to keep it safe, she turned around to each of the four winds, feeling with her club and sniffing with her nose. Tawhaki and Karihi kept well clear of that old lady's club.

When she sat down again on the club, Karihi gave her a light slap on the cheek. Quite frightened, Whaitiri put both her hands to her face and cried out: 'Who did that?'

Then Tawhaki placed two pieces of moistened clay against her eyes, uttering the karakia that begins:

> Irimata, irimata,
> weromata, weromata,
> he wai o mata ki te ra . . .

Her sight was at once restored, and she saw quite plainly, and recognised her grandchildren, and wept over them. When their greetings were completed Whaitiri asked the brothers where they were going.

'I am going to look for my little daughter,' said Tawhaki.

Whaitiri was sitting on the ground counting taro

'But where is she?' asked Whaitiri.

'Up there in the heavens,' said Tawhaki.

'What made her go up there?' Whaitiri asked.

'Her mother came from there,' Tawhaki replied.

'Ha,' said the old woman. 'Then yonder lies your road.' And she pointed to the tendrils of a great creeper that hung from the heavens. 'But do not start to climb up there so late in the day,' she said. 'You had better wait until the morning.'

So the brothers stayed that night with Whaitiri, and their slave cooked food for them. In the morning, when this man had again prepared food for them, Tawhaki presented him to Whaitiri in return for her kindness.

'There is your road,' said the old woman, pointing to the tendrils. 'But take care you do not look down when you are half way up, or you will become giddy and fall. Be careful also that you do not take hold of a tendril that is hanging loose. Hold only those that have struck roots in the earth.' Then Tawhaki understood the meaning of the words that Hapai had spoken as she was leaving his house.

'If you fall down,' said the old woman, 'you will be good for me to eat.'

Karihi was the first to begin climbing. He went up some way, and Tawhaki said a karakia for his safety. But by mistake Karihi took hold of a tendril that had no roots in the earth. A blast of wind swung him away, out to the very horizon. Then a wind sprang up from the sea and swung him back again. As he passed close to the earth Tawhaki called out: 'Now, brother, now is the time to jump. Let go!' Karihi did so, and stood beside Tawhaki once more.

'You said a karakia and made me fall,' said Karihi, who was shaken and annoyed. So the brothers had words about this. But Tawhaki, who did not want Karihi to come to harm, said to him: 'I would like you to go home now and care for our families.' So Karihi returned to the village of their tribe, and Tawhaki went on his way alone. By remembering what he had been told, and by reciting certain powerful karakia he had learnt from Tuna roa, he succeeded in climbing up. These are the words Tawhaki spoke as he passed through the several heavens:

> Ascend, Tawhaki, to the first heaven,
> let the fair sky consent.
> Ascend, Tawhaki, to the second heaven,
> let the fair sky consent.

Ascend, Tawhaki, to the third heaven,
let the fair sky consent.
Ascend, Tawhaki, to the fourth heaven,
let the fair sky consent.
Ascend, Tawhaki, to the fifth heaven,
let the fair sky consent.
Ascend, Tawhaki, to the sixth heaven,
let the fair sky consent.
Ascend, Tawhaki, to the seventh heaven,
let the fair sky consent.
Ascend, Tawhaki, to the eighth heaven,
Iet the fair sky consent.
Ascend, Tawhaki, to the ninth heaven,
let the fair sky consent.
Ascend, Tawhaki, to the un-numbered heaven,
let the fair sky consent.
    Cling, cling, like the lizard to the rafters!
Stick, stick, close to the side of heaven.

TAWHAKI IS REUNITED WITH HAPAI

WHEN Tawhaki reached the topmost heaven he disguised his handsome appearance and his youth. He assumed the likeness of an ugly old man in tattered clothing, and in this state he was seen by his brothers-in-law, the relatives of Hapai. They were at work on the hull of a new canoe, and one of them, seeing him, called out: 'Hullo, there's an old man who will be useful for us.' So the old man sat down and watched them adzing out the canoe. It was being made from the trunk of a very large tree, which they had cut down the year before and seasoned in the ground. As evening approached they called him and said: 'Old man! Come and carry these adzes for us, will you?'

Tawhaki, amused at being spoken to in that way by common people, gathered the adzes up, but he said to the young men: 'You go on. I cannot walk as fast as you.' So they left him and as soon as they were out of sight Tawhaki resumed his noble form and all his strength. And taking an adze he went swiftly to work on their canoe. Beginning at the bow, he worked towards the stern on one side. Then he worked from stern to bow along the other side. The canoe was soon finished on the outside, except for its end-pieces, which still had to be shaped and fitted. Then he became the grubby old man again, and trudged off to the village with the tools.

Near the village he was seen by two servant women who were gathering firewood. 'Here's a queer old man,' said one of them. 'Let's make him carry our firewood.' So they laid a load of firewood on the old man's back, and made this chief carry that as well as the adzes.

At the village, Tawhaki saw Hapai sitting with his daughter.

He put down the adzes and the firewood and went straight towards her. The people called out: 'Don't go there! It is tapu where Hapai sits and you will be tapu if you go there!'

He took no notice, but sat on the ground near Hapai, and remained there until it was night. After they had eaten food in the morning the brothers-in-law came to him and said: 'Old man! Carry the adzes again, will you? Take them to where the canoe is being made.'

When the work-party reached the spot the young men were astonished to see the state of their canoe. They all gathered round to look and no one could offer any explanation, so they worked away at the inside for the rest of that day. Towards evening they told the old man to carry the adzes again, and Tawhaki did as before. He hung behind, and when they were out of sight he swiftly finished off the inside of their canoe. Then he returned to the village and sat by Hapai once more.

On the third morning the young men again made Tawhaki carry their adzes to the work-site, and once more were astonished to see what had been done in the night. After wondering about it for a time they set to work on the timbers that had been cut to form the haumi, or end-pieces of the canoe. But during the day some of them decided to see what the old man did when their backs were turned. At evening, therefore, they left for the village as usual, having told Tawhaki to bring the adzes. After going some distance a party of them turned back and went by another path to a spot from where they could watch without being seen. They saw no old man, but a handsome person of chiefly appearance, who was working with uncanny speed to finish off the end-pieces. 'Just come and look at this,' said those who saw him first. 'He is not in the least like that old man.' They knew then that the person they were watching must be one of the gods, and they hurried back to the village with this news.

They went at once to Hapai and asked her to describe her husband. She described a man like the one they had just seen.

Tawhaki was working with uncanny speed

'Then that must be Tawhaki,' she said. 'That chief must certainly be your brother-in-law.' Soon afterwards the old man trudged into the village, carrying the adzes. Hapai stood up and went to him. 'Now tell me, who are you?' she said.

Tawhaki made no reply but walked straight on towards her house, where her little daughter was sitting.

'Tell me,' said Hapai, 'are you Tawhaki?'

The old man grunted 'Hu!' and then there was a gasp from the people watching as he stooped down and picked up Hapai's little daughter, and pressed her to his bosom. Some ran out of the marae in fright, others remained, and there were murmurs of pleasure and astonishment as the figure of the old man straightened up, and Tawhaki, the perfect chief, appeared before them in all his splendour. Tawhaki and Hapai then retired into their house together.

'I have come so that our little daughter may have her naming ceremony performed,' said Tawhaki. 'Let her have the proper ceremonies for the daughter of a chief, to secure good fortune and happiness.'

Hapai agreed, and on the following day an opening was broken through the rear wall of the house. The little girl's rank was shown by her being carried out that way instead of through the common door. When the naming ceremony had been performed over Puanga, lightning flashed from the armpits of Tawhaki, and all were made aware of who he was.

These were the words spoken at the naming ceremony of Puanga:

> Clear the great courtyards,
> clear the long courtyards,
> the courtyards of the daughter.
> Baptize Puanga in this water
> at the source of the stream of Puanga
> in this world.
> Move; yes, moving,
> closing quite near.
> Baptize with a wave,
> turning away.

here in charge of the kumara plots. At the proper season, when the moon is new, he will emerge, and will devour men as his food.' 'All that is true,' said Rata, 'but how does Matuku know when the moon is new if he lives below?' 'I call aloud to him,' the man replied. 'And when will the moon be new?' asked Rata. The man who was in charge of the place said: 'In two nights hence. You had better go back to your own village now, but on the morning of the second day from this, return to me.'

Rata did so, and on the second day he returned to the man and asked him: 'Will you show me some spot where I can hide myself from the enemy I am about to fight with?' The man took him to a place where there were two springs of clear water. 'He will rise out of this ground on which we are standing,' the man said. 'That pool is the one in which he washes his hair, and that other is the one he uses to reflect his face while he dresses it. You cannot kill him at that one, because he would be able to see your reflection in the water. But at the one he washes in you could get close to him.' 'And he will come out of the ground this evening?' Rata asked. The man replied: 'He will.'

After the sun had gone down and the crescent of the moon could just be seen, Rata concealed himself not far from the spring he had been shown. The man who had been left there for the purpose then shouted in a loud voice: 'Hou! The moon is new, Matuku, it is time.' Then the ground trembled with the weight of Matuku's feet, and he rose up straight from the earth with a terrible growl, and spoke these words,

> Piro, piro,
> haungaunga,
> taku kai he tangata!

of which the meaning is 'A smell, a smell, a stinking smell, a man for me to eat!' But seeing his own man there, and being assured that all was well, Matuku went to the washing pool. He laid his taiaha upon the ground, and kneeling down on both knees he unbound his hair and shook it out, and plunged it in the pool. Rata, creeping forward, took up Matuku's taiaha, the very weapon that had killed Wahieroa. 'My father's blood,' he said as he gripped the staff, 'was on this taiaha.' Then, as Matuku raised himself from the water, Rata with one hand seized him by the hair, and with the other slew that cannibal, and so avenged his father's death.

It now remained for Rata to find the bones of Wahieroa and take them home. He asked the keeper of the place where those bones were, and the man replied: 'They are not here. A strange people who live in another place came here and carried them off. They live below the sea, those people.'

Rata therefore returned to his village, the home of Tawhaki and of the jealous cousins who had tried to kill Tawhaki at the pool of Rangituhi; and he considered how he might recover the bones of his father, since until this was accomplished he could not say to himself, 'My act is complete.'

One day his mother went gathering firewood. When she returned she handed her son some twigs of a tree that she had seen. 'I saw a fine totara tree,' she said. 'Tomorrow you must go and see it.' This was her way of informing Rata of what he must do, to complete his task; for a fine large totara means a fine canoe. He went into the forest and saw the tree, and afterwards he asked his mother: 'What action shall I take?' For answer, she gave him some stone adzes, but these adzes were blunt. 'Go and hold them against the back of your ancestress Hine tu a hoanga,' his mother said. 'She will say "Be sharpened, be sharpened," then they will be sharp and you can lash their handles on.'

Rata took the adzes to Hine-of-the-Whetstone-Back, and did as his mother had directed him. Then he carried them into the forest, to the totara tree which his mother had found. It was straight throughout its trunk, with a branching top that began high up—a mighty tree for a great canoe. He cut it down at once, and lopped off its branches, and worked at it throughout that day. But in his haste to begin Rata had neglected to say the proper chants to Tane, the forest god. And the inhabitants of the forest, the innumerable multitude of creatures who are called Te Tini o te Hakuturi, became angry for this reason. In the night they all came and took the tree and raised it up again. They sang this chant of their own while they did their work; in a confused clamour of all those twittering and insect voices that are heard in the forest, they sang these words:

> Fly together, chips and splinters,
> stick you fast together!
> Arise and stand again,
> a fresh-grown tree!

They restored the tree, to the last little bit of its foliage, and next morning when Rata returned he could find no sign of his labour. The tree his mother saw was standing there, to be sure, but the one he felled was nowhere to be seen. Bewildered, and supposing himself to be the victim of some delusion, he set to work again. He felled the tree, cut off its branching top, and hollowed it, and shaped the hull. When it became too dark to work any more he returned to the village.

As soon as he was gone, the Thousands of the Hakuturi came out from their little places and once again they raised the tree. Throughout the night they twittered and chirruped, and clicked and whistled, and sang their working chants, and in the morning there stood a fresh-grown tree, as on the previous day. When he had eaten food at home, Rata returned once more with his adzes. He was astonished to find that tree exactly as if he had not touched it. But he realised now that he had not been mistaken. There must be others in the forest, who undid his work. He decided to fell the tree again and do his normal work till daylight went, and then to hide. At evening he put his adzes on his shoulder and went off as if to the village. But then he turned back, and hid himself in the undergrowth. He had not been there very long when he heard the multitude of Tane's offspring all converging on the spot, singing their chants as they came. As soon as they had gathered round the tree, Rata rushed out and seized a number of them in his hands. In their fright at this, the Hakuturi's Thousands made so much noise that some of the trees themselves became alarmed, and bent down with their heads to the ground. They have never been able to raise themselves again; and so it came about that the ponga, or tree-fern, the kareao, or supplejack, and other plants, are all bowed down.

'So it is you!' said Rata when the commotion had died down. 'It's you who have been interfering with my tree!' 'But it is not your tree, O Rata,' they replied. 'You had no right to cut it down. You did not say the chants to Tane that are necessary before you started. Had you done so, we would not have had to raise it up again.'

Rata felt ashamed, and the Hakuturi's Thousands saw that he regretted his offence. He told them then for what purpose he wanted the tree, and when they heard this they felt regard for this man who intended to recover the bones of a father he had never known. So they told him to return to his village and said that they would finish the canoe for him.

He obeyed them, and departed, and as soon as he was gone they all set to work to complete what Rata had begun. There were so many of them, and they understood each other so well, that no sooner had they started than they were finished. They did everything that was required. They fitted the canoe with flooring slats and thwarts, and added the rauawa, or gunwale strakes, to raise the sides and give more free-board. At the prow they put a tauihu, a grotesque figure-head with its tongue out, and at the stern they put an upright piece, the taurapa, both intricately carved. They put battens over the top-strake seams, and made the lashings tight. They attached white feathers of the albatross at intervals along the seams, and other ornaments they placed at the bow and stern. When all these things had been properly fixed in place, and carvings completed on the thwarts, and paddles and bailers made, the Hakuturi's Thousands gave the canoe a name. It was Punui, meaning Great Original; though later the canoe was called Riwaru, and Pakawai, and had other names as well.

Then Rata came, with men, to take delivery and haul Punui to the sea. But they found the bush so dense that they could not get it out by any ordinary means. It would not move from where it was. They therefore said this karakia:

> Thrust aside the thicket,
> thrust aside the bramble,
> and Whiti and Matuku
> shall come forth.

And this is the saying for the start of a quarrel—'Break the barriers down and anger will burst out.' For Whiti and Matuku were notorious for their harshness.

When Rata's men sang that chant the thicket opened, but the canoe would still not move. They heaved and hauled, but all in vain. Rata had dammed the stream to raise it, but there was not sufficient water to float Punui. So they uttered chants to Rangi and Tawhiri, to send the rains. These gods did so, and the stream became a torrent, it floated Punui, and Rata's men guided it down-stream to the sea, and it floated well.

Then Rata embarked with a hundred and forty warriors, and set off for the place where the Ponaturi had their house, Manawa Tane. When they reached it Rata went ashore alone. It was strange, flat, marshy country, where the vegetation was all sedges, flax and raupo, with toetoe, the pampas grass, and ti whanake, the tree now called the cabbage tree. He crept along, his footsteps covered by the rattling of the ti whanake leaves and all the flax that was blowing in the sea breeze. He saw that a fire was burning in the tuaahu, or sacred place of the Ponaturi. He therefore hid himself among the flax bushes and listened, for some aged priests of the Ponaturi were chanting there, and conducting some horrid ceremony.

Now those tohunga were making use in their ceremony of the

Then Rata embarked with his warriors

bones of Wahieroa. They were knocking them together while they uttered an extremely tapu chant known only to themselves, the name of which was Titikura. Rata listened to this chant and learnt it off by heart. When he was sure that he had memorised it he rushed out and slew those tohunga. They were too surprised to defend themselves or call for help, and very soon Rata was running back to his canoe with the bones of his father.

In the morning the Ponaturi found their priests lying dead at the sacred place, just as Rata had left them. They at once set out for Rata's land. They marched, the whole thousand of them, into the sea, and rushed along its bottom until they came up on the beach near Rata's village. An engagement took place immediately, and Rata's men, outnumbered, were very soon getting the worst of it. Sixty men of Rata's tribe lay dead, when Rata suddenly remembered Titikura, the dreadful spell that he had learned from the tohunga of his enemies. He spoke this chant, and all his casualties were at once restored to life. They sprang up and rushed back into the fight, and in this way the Ponaturi were defeated by Rata's men, the whole thousand of them were slain. This was the second time that the Ponaturi were utterly destroyed.

After these matters had been concluded, and the Ponaturi burned, the men of Rata's tribe hauled up Punui on the shore, and roofed it over with thatch to protect it from the sun and rain.

PART TWO

TRADITIONS OF THE MIGRATION

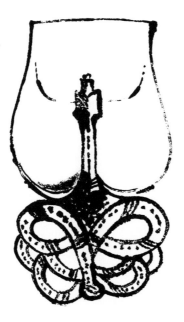

Matahorua is the canoe, Kupe is the chief, and Reti is the navigator. With this canoe a large part of the Great Ocean of Kiwa was explored, and these islands were discovered by Kupe.

KUPE'S DISCOVERY OF AOTEAROA

IT was the demigod Maui who fished up these islands from the bottom of the sea, but it was Kupe who discovered them, and returned to Hawaiki with news of a land inhabited only by birds. The voyage of Kupe came about in this way. There was in Hawaiki a very great canoe-builder named Toto, who had two daughters. He went to cut down a fine large tree on the banks of the lake called Waiharakeke, and when it fell this tree split lengthwise into two equal parts. Toto therefore made two great ocean canoes, one of which he named Aotea and gave to his daughter Rongo-rongo, and the other he named Matahorua and gave to his daughter Kura marotini.

Now Kura marotini was the wife of Kupe's young cousin Hotu-rapa, and Kupe desired her. One day Kupe and Hoturapa were out fishing, a long way from the shore, when Kupe's line got caught on a snag. Being accustomed to giving orders, he said to his cousin: 'Hotu, my line is caught on something. Just dive down and loosen it for me, would you?' Hotu took hold of the line and said: 'Let me see if I can't loosen it.' 'It's no use,' said Kupe, 'I've tried, it won't come. Just dive down, go on.'

So Hoturapa jumped over and dived. But as soon as he was gone Kupe cut the anchor rope, threw the rest of his line into the sea, and paddled quickly for the shore. When Hotu came up again the canoe was far away. 'E Kupe!' he cried, 'Kupe! Come back and get me!'

They named it Aotearoa

The whole thing was a trick on Kupe's part to get rid of Hotu and have his wife. Hoturapa was drowned, and Kupe made off with Kura marotini. But her relations were suspicious about the accident, and to escape their vengeance Kupe decided to leave Hawaiki. And so, in her canoe Matahorua, taking his own family, and Reti as the priest and navigator, he set off into that part of the Ocean known as Te Tiritiri o te Moana, Share of Ocean. It was thus that Kupe came to explore this part of the Great Ocean of Kiwa, and found these islands that now are called Aotearoa.

After they had sailed for many days, keeping a constant watch for any sign of land, such as a patch of different colour on the underside of the clouds, or a cloud of unusual shape, it fell to Hine te aparangi, wife of Kupe, to be the first to see something. She cried, 'He ao! He ao!' and the land beneath the cloud, when they sailed along it, was found to be much longer than any island those people had ever known. They therefore named it Aotearoa, Long White Cloud.

As he was going down the east coast of the north island Kupe passed close to a small projecting piece of land.* In a large cave there a wheke, or giant octopus, had its home, and Kupe surprised this wheke. Frightened by the sight of a canoe with men in it, the wheke left its cave and fled before the bows of Matahorua, turning round the bottom of the island in the direction of Raukawa.† Thus Kupe found the opening between the two islands of this land. He passed Cape Terawhiti and crossed the strait to look at the land on the other side. Finding the opening at Te Awaiti, he went into it and encountered a very strong current, to which he gave the name Kura te au. Strong as it was, Kupe made his paddlers fight that current, and he entered Te Awaiti.

Now the wheke, whose name was Te Wheke a Muturangi, had gone there to hide. And when it heard the canoe approaching, and the paddling chants of Kupe's men as they struggled against the current, it raised its enormous arms above the water and slapped its suckers against the sides of Matahorua, to devour her and her crew. Then followed a great sea battle between the wheke and this chief. Kupe took up the adze Rakatuwhenua, which he had with him, and with fierce strokes he slashed at the wheke's many limbs. When the wheke had laid them over the sides of the canoe Kupe sliced bits off them, and his people ate them, but the monster took no notice at all. It writhed and lurched, and lashed about, and the canoe was in danger of being swamped in that rapid current. Then Kupe thought of a way to deceive the wheke. Dropping his adze, he picked up a large hollow gourd that had been full of drinking water. He threw it overboard, and the wheke, thinking

* Castle Point   † Cook Strait

The Wheke raised its arms above the water ➤

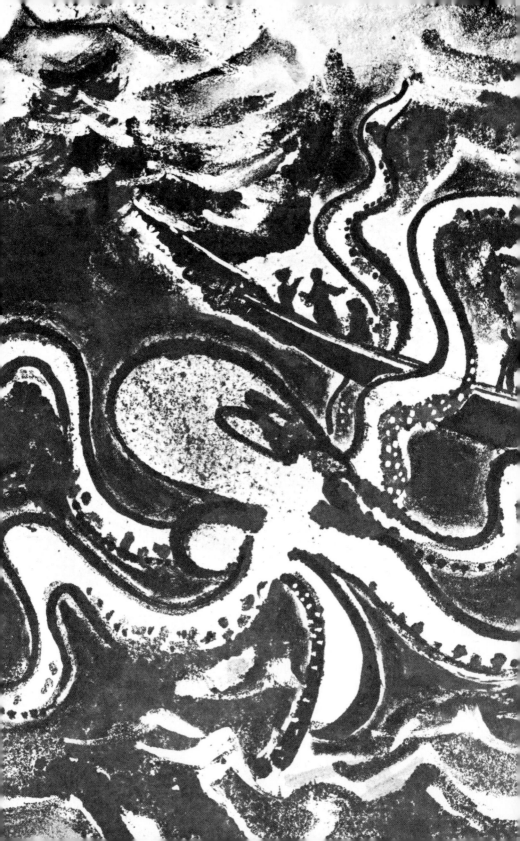

it was a man, let go the canoe and seized the gourd. Then Kupe took his adze again, and when the wheke's head and vital parts were wrapped around the gourd he severed it in two with one tremendous blow. Thus died the wheke of Muturangi.

After this, Kupe also severed the island of Aropawa from the south island, and the islands of Kapiti and Mana from the north. That is to say, he sailed in through Te Awaiti and around Aropawa island, and then up the west coast of the north island on the inside of Kapiti and Mana. And this old chant recalls these facts:

> I sing, I sing of Kupe,
> the man who severed the land!
> Kapiti stands apart,
> Mana stands apart,
> Aropawa stands apart.
> These are the signs
> of my ancestor Kupe,
> who discovered Titapua,
> who explored the land.

Kupe stayed a short time at Whanganui a Tara, the great harbour of Tara,* and two small islands in it were named after two of his daughters, Matiu and Makoro, who were with him. It is said also that another of his daughters, Taiapua, killed herself at the red cliff Tamure, outside the western heads of the harbour. Kupe went there to bewail her death, and cut his forehead with a piece of obsidian, as was the custom, to show his grief. The blood of this chief stained the rocks all red, and they are red today, as can be seen by those who pass that way.

It was after this that Kupe travelled up the coast to the place where Patea now stands. He set up a post there to mark his visit, and he heard the voices of the only two inhabitants of this country he ever spoke of. He heard the cry of the kokako, or crow, and he

* Wellington

saw the little tiwaiwaka, which flicked about in front of his face and snapped its tiny beak, and fanned out its black-and-white tail.

Now Kupe's work was this, that he discovered these islands and some of the openings, the harbours and rivers, and to some of them he gave names. On his return to Hawaiki he spoke of the great land of high mists which he had seen. When he was asked if there were people there he replied, he saw only kokako and tiwai-waka. This was more polite than saying 'No'. When he was asked if he intended to return, he replied 'E hoki Kupe?'—'Will Kupe return?'—which down to this day is used as a way of saying no.

*　　*　　*

Kupe's friend Ngahue travelled with him. Ngahue left Hawaiki because of the quarrel between obsidian and greenstone. Ngahue owned the block of greenstone which was called Pounamu, or sometimes 'The Fish of Ngahue', and Hine tu a hoanga became enraged. Her fish or stone was waiapu, or obsidian. She drove him out, and Ngahue, seeking a resting place for his greenstone, travelled to Tuhua. But Hine-of-the-Whetstone-Back pursued him, and to escape her again he came to this land, Aotearoa. He travelled beyond the places Kupe visited, and carried his greenstone to Arahura, on the western coast of the south island, or Te Wai Pounamu. There he made an everlasting resting-place for his greenstone.

He broke a piece off it, and taking it with him he returned to Hawaiki, and reported that he had found a country which produced pounamu in abundance and also the very large bird called moa, standing higher than a man. According to some persons he killed one of these moa, and put it in a taha, or calabash, and carried it back to Hawaiki. From his greenstone Ngahue made the sharp adzes Tutauru and Hauhau te rangi. From the little pieces that were chipped away many precious ornaments of chiefs were manufactured. The eardrop Kaukaumatua was one of these. This was in the possession of Te Heuheu, and was only lost as recently as 1846, when he and many of his people were killed by a landslide.

Aotea is the canoe, Turi is the chief, and Tapo is the priest. From the people of this canoe are descended the Whanganui tribes and the Ngati Ruanui.

THE MIGRATION OF TURI TO AOTEAROA

WHILE Kupe was away from Hawaiki on his voyage of discovery a quarrel arose between Turi and the high chief Uenuku, which led to Turi's leaving Hawaiki in the canoe Aotea. This was the second of the two canoes that Toto built, being made from the other half of the tree from which Matahorua had come. It belonged to Turi's wife, Rongorongo, who was the daughter of Toto and sister of Kura marotini.

The quarrel between Turi and Uenuku began when Turi, after getting in his kumara crop, sent Uenuku a portion as his atinga, or tribute, and Uenuku took the smallness of the gift as an insult. The tribute was carried to Uenuku by a little boy named Potiki roroa. Some say that this child was Turi's son. When Uenuku saw how small a portion of the crop had been set aside for him, he killed the boy who brought it, and devoured him.

Then Turi set his mind upon revenge. He decided that the most satisfying form of utu would be to kill Uenuku's own small son, whose name was Oe potiki. In the hope of enticing him to come out he set all the children of his own family to whipping tops, throwing the teka, and other games, on a piece of ground where Oe potiki could see them. This did not work; but later, on a day that was very hot, the children of Turi's household all went bathing in the river, and this time Oe potiki came out to join them. Then Turi snatched him and split his head with a club. The body of this child was eaten by Turi and his friends, but the manawa, or heart and lungs, were kept aside and when some women were carrying gifts of food to Uenuku, Turi handed them a basket of baked kumara, with the manawa of Oe potiki, cut up and cooked as a relish in the middle.

Uenuku had not yet learned the fate of his son, and as he sat down to the feast he sighed: 'Poor little Oe potiki, how he would have liked this delicious food; but he no longer comes to sit and eat beside me.' After he had eaten, one of Uenuku's friends who had been told about it said to him: 'They have made you eat the manawa of Oe potiki.' He answered with the saying, 'Very well, he lies in the belly of Toi,' meaning that there would be a dreadful revenge. But he showed no other sign of feeling, lest he satisfy his enemy.

Turi then was living in his house Rangiatea, and his wife, Rongorongo, had a new baby daughter, whose name was Tane roroa. One night Rongorongo went outside to feed her baby and she heard Uenuku singing a chant about Oe potiki:

> Bring me the thousands,
> bring me the many,
> bring me all the Ngati rongotea!
> Let Oe potiki work death.
> The first revenge is sweet!
> Assemble here!
> Let all who hear assemble!

She went to Turi and told him, and Turi at once knew what this meant. He knew that Uenuku was planning a great revenge for the murder of his son and for being made to eat his heart.

Now Kupe had by this time returned to Hawaiki, and when Turi heard of the land he had discovered, this land of high mists inhabited only by birds, he decided to come to Aotearoa. He therefore embarked with all his family in his wife's canoe, the Aotea, and from Kupe he received the directions. 'Mind that you keep sailing to the east,' said Kupe, 'where the sun rises. Keep your bow pointing always in that direction.' Yet Turi reached these islands in spite of this advice. He tried to persuade Kupe to accompany him, but Kupe replied with the saying which we still use, 'E hoki Kupe?', which means in the pakeha's words, 'Not I!'

'When you get there,' said Kupe, 'you had better go at once to the river I found. Its mouth opens to the west, on that side of the island. You will find there only two inhabitants. One carries its tail straight up and sticking out. Do not mistake the voice of the other for a man, it cries out just like one. If you stand on the other side of the river and call out to them, you will hear them answering you from the other side. That will be the place I found.' This place that Kupe spoke of is the mouth of the Patea river.

In his haste to get away Turi nearly forgot to take on board the two great steering paddles that belonged to the Aotea—their names were Kautu ki te rangi and Te Rokuowhiti—and also the two bailing scoops, Tipua horonuku and Rangi ke wheriko. They were fetched for him by his brother-in-law Tuau, and when Tuau had put them on board Turi said to him: 'Just come out a little way and see me started.' Good-naturedly, Tuau agreed and went on board, intending to leave the canoe as it passed the harbour opening.

And so the Aotea left Hawaiki, carrying some seed kumara of the variety called kakau; some edible rats in cages, and some tame

Carrying some edible rats

some pukeko, or swamp-hen . . .

green parrots; some pukeko, or swamp-hen; and seeds for growing
the gourd, or calabash, and many other necessary things for
founding a new settlement. Hence the name of that canoe, 'Aotea
of the precious cargo'. There were also taken certain gods, in the
form of the carved sticks in which their spirits lived, including
Maru. The adze Te Awhiorangi, too, is said to have been brought
here in the Aotea.

As they left the shore in the late afternoon Tuau sat in the stern
paddling, as a gesture, to help his brother-in-law on his way. Near
the harbour entrance Turi said to him: 'You come to the middle
here and let me paddle,' which Tuau did. But soon he found that
they had gone well past the headland where he intended to get out,
and Turi, who was short of crew, paid no attention when he was
asked to stop. Thus Tuau was carried off by a trick of Turi's, and
left Hawaiki grieving for his family, lest they think he had deserted
them.

When daylight came, Tapo, the priest and navigator of that
canoe, became insolent and disobedient to his chief (some say

because of Turi's trickery to Tuau) and Turi had him thrown over the side. When Tapo found himself in the sea he called out cheerfully: 'Come on, Turi, let me live in the world a little longer,' as if it was all a joke. From his manner Turi realised that Tapo must be under the protection of Maru, one of the gods they had brought with them; and Maru, in fact, let Turi know that he was angry, for Turi distinctly heard the god say: 'If you go without my servant you will never reach Nukuroa'. Not to anger Maru any further, he therefore turned about, and took that navigator on board again.

And so they sailed across the ocean, in the direction of these islands and not towards the east as Kupe had directed. When they had been at sea for some days and had been through some heavy weather, the Aotea's seams began to open. Water from the waves was pouring through the cracks beneath the topstrakes, the bailers were hard at it day and night, and Turi was constantly reciting chants to keep the canoe afloat. At last they sighted the small rocky island of Rangitahua.* They landed there, and replaced the lashings and caulking of their topstrakes, and refitted the whole canoe. It is said they also obtained some berries of the karaka tree and brought them to this land. If this is so, then they were there in the month of March.

Now another canoe was travelling in company with Aotea. It was called Te Ririno, and its chief was Potoru. This canoe also landed at Rangitahua. It was carrying some dogs, to supply both food and clothing for the chiefs in their new country. On Rangitahua they killed two of these dogs, Whakapapa tuakura and Tangi kakariki. One, they cut up and offered as a sacrifice to the gods, and the other they cooked and shared amongst themselves. When they had eaten, they unwrapped a sacred cloak called Hunakiko and spread it on the ground, and called upon the gods to see them safely over the last part of their journey. They set up posts to the gods on that island, and removed all bad luck from the canoes by

* One of the Kermadecs, to the north-east of New Zealand.

saying over them the prayers Keuenga, Takanga, and Whaka inuinumanga. After that they were ready to embark.

Then there was a great argument down on the shore between Turi and Potoru, the chiefs of the two canoes. They had different ideas about the proper sailing directions. Turi was for sailing east, according to Kupe's strict advice, and Potoru was for heading in the direction where the sun went down. Turi kept repeating what Kupe had said, but Potoru insisted that they must travel west; so Turi gave in, and it is said that they left Rangitahua on a south-west course. As a result of this the Ririno was wrecked on a reef in that island group, and hence the popular saying about the 'obstinacy of Potoru'.

Now Potoru was right, of course. But after this Turi set his canoe toward the rising sun, and still reached Aotearoa. During this last part of the voyage Turi's wife Rongorongo gave birth to a son, whom they named Tutawa. By this time they had only nine of their kumara left. Turi offered one of them to the gods to secure protection for Tutawa. He touched the roof of the baby's mouth with it and spoke the appropriate prayers and cast it into the sea, and then sailed on. Some days later they sighted land, and even at that time there was trouble on board. One of the crew, a man named Tuanui a te ra, who had a crooked foot, was disobedient and insolent to Turi, so he was thrown overboard.

At last the Aotea was run ashore on the western side of the north island, in a little harbour north of Kawhia to which the name Aotea was given.* One of the first things the voyagers saw when they walked on the beach to stretch their legs was the crooked footprint of a man—none other than Tuanui a te ra.

They rested for a while and then, leaving Aotea in the harbour, set off to the south to look for the river running west that Kupe had described. One party, Turi sent ahead under Pungarehu, with stones from some of their karaka berries, to be planted on the way. Then Turi followed with another party, crossing many rivers

* Raglan

facing west and giving them the names they bear today. He skirted round Kawhia harbour and named it. He crossed what we call the Mokau river, naming it Moekau from his sleeping there. The Waitara he named from the wide steps he took when fording its mouth. At two places he spread out the sacred cloak or kura called Hunakiko, and from this act those places were named Oakura and Maraekura. To other places also, Turi gave the names that are written down in the book by Governor Grey.

At last Turi reached the river mouth that Kupe had described, and there he built a pa, or fortified village, which he called Rangi-tawhi. It is said that there were no inhabitants when Kupe came to these islands, yet Turi built a pa. He erected a post there which he called Whakatopea, a house which he named Matangirei, and a latrine called Paepae hakehake. His whata, or storehouse, he named Paeahua, and the well he dug was Parara ki te uru. To the river itself he gave its name, Patea.

At this settlement Turi planted his kumara seed. Because of the sacrifice at sea, they had now only eight. These they divided into pieces and planted separately, and when the shoots came up Turi used the chant called Ahuroa to make the ground tapu and pro-mote the plants. As a result, in due season they lifted eight hundred baskets of kumara from that kumara plot.

In this way Turi took possession of this part of the land that Kupe found. Rongorongo was his principal wife, and from their children sprang the tribes of the Whanganui district, and the Ngati Ruanui.

Before the Arawa canoe left Hawaiki there were dreadful quarrels over food-stealing. On the one side were the high chief Uenuku and Toi te huatahi, and on the other side were the two young sons of Houmai tawhiti, Tama te kapua and Whakaturia.

THE QUARRELS IN HAWAIKI

THIS quarrel began over an act of sacrilege that was done to Uenuku by a dog belonging to Houmai tawhiti. Houmai was a venerable chief of Hawaiki who knew that men must try to live in peace. His neighbouring chief Uenuku was that cruel man we have heard of, who ate the flesh of children.

Houmai's dog was called Potaka tawhiti, and what it did was this: it licked the scab off a leg-sore of Uenuku's and ate it, in front of Toi. A dog making food of the person of a *chief*! So Toi and Uenuku killed the dog, and soon it was missed by Houmai's two young sons, whose names were Tama te kapua and Whakaturia. Though young as yet, these two were great big strong youths, tall and proud. They suspected that someone had stolen their dog to eat him. They went from village to village looking for him, calling 'Moi, moi! Moi, moi!' wherever they thought he might be tied up. They came to Toi's house, and there they heard Potaka's muffled barking: 'Ao, ao! Ao, ao!' They could not see the dog anywhere, but when they asked Toi about it they realised that it was inside the fat belly of that chief. They called 'Moi, moi,' again, and the dog knew them, and barked 'Ao, ao!' in answer. Toi, putting his hand over his mouth, tried to hush it, and this gave rise to the saying, when something comes to light and has to be admitted by the one concealing it: 'I thought I had hidden you in the belly of Toi, but there you are still howling away.'

There are some who declare that Toi had the hiccups. At all events, Tama accused him of having killed Potaka, and asked him:

'Why did you not kill the dog, if you were angry, and bring him back to me, so that we would both have been satisfied and could have remained good friends? Well,' he added as he walked away, 'you will be hearing more of this.' Then he and Whakaturia returned to their own village, considering how to take utu for their dog.

When they got home they set to work to make a pair of stilts, and after dark they returned to the village of Toi and Uenuku. Near his house Uenuku had a splendid breadfruit tree that stood far higher than his roof, and many of its fruit were ripe. With Whakaturia keeping watch below, Tama walked on the stilts to reach the fruit, and threw them down to his brother, and they did this for several nights running, without being seen. Then Uenuku's people noticed that the ripe fruit were disappearing. They found no footprints, only the marks of a pair of stilts. So they set a watch, and that night they caught the two young men. Whakaturia they seized on the ground without difficulty, but Tama with his big strides got down to the sea before they caught up with him.

'Chop him down and let's see him fall into the water!' some of them cried above the surf, and everyone agreed that this would be a good idea, including Tama.

'Yes,' he called down to them in the darkness, 'bring me down in the waves and it won't hurt so much. If you do it up on the shore, the fall will kill me!' For Tama knew perfectly well that if they brought him down in the water he would have no chance to escape, whereas on land he would be able to run for it. So they changed their minds, as he meant them to. They led him to the shore to chop him down, and with their adzes they cut away the stilts. Although the fall was heavy, it was not in water, and before anyone knew what was happening, Tama was off into the night. They still had Whakaturia tied up at the village, so they all went back and gathered round to see him put to death.

'Kill him now,' said some of them, but there were others who wanted to do something to make up for losing Tama te kapua.

'No, let's string him up in the roof of Uenuku's meeting house and smoke him to death,' these others cried. This was agreed to, so Whakaturia was put into a large flax basket and hoisted up to the rafters, in the smoke of the fires. Then they all started their usual evening's entertainment of singing and dancing, and this was the worst part of Whakaturia's punishment, for both the music and the dancing were shockingly bad, in no way up to the standard he was used to in his father's village.

Whakaturia remained there, enduring the smoke and discomfort and the inferior entertainment, and after a few nights Houmai said to Tama: 'There's your brother hung up there in Uenuku's house, almost stifled with the smoke. Why don't you go and see how he is?' So Tama went that night, and stealthily climbed the thatch while all inside were singing. He made a hole through the reeds just where his brother was, and whispered:

'Are you dead?'

'No,' said Whakaturia huskily, 'I'm still alive.'

'What is their singing like here?' asked Tama. 'Do they dance well?'

'No,' said Whakaturia, 'I've never heard worse. Even their own people criticise it all the time.'

'Well,' said Tama, 'what about calling out and complaining? Let them think the smoke isn't affecting you. Tell them that you've never heard worse singing or seen worse dancing. They'll probably say "Can you do better?" or something like that. Tell them you can, and get them to let you down to show them. Then you could say you're filthy with soot and so on, and ask for a comb and oil before you start. Then ask for a maro, and put it on, and get them to give you Uenuku's taiaha, and then start dancing. Then tell them to open the door and give you air. I'll go down and wait outside, and when you dance your way out of the door I will be ready to bolt it up.'

So Tama climbed down and waited about outside, and at the end of that group of items he heard his brother's voice call down to the

They led him to the shore to chop him down

people in the house. A voice called for silence, and someone else cried out: 'That fellow's alive up there! What's he saying?'

'I said you don't know any decent songs, and your dancing's awful,' Whakaturia called down in a muffled voice.

'Ho!' came an answer from below, from the person in charge of the programme, 'then you think your people can do better, do you?'

'I can do better myself,' said Whakaturia. 'The singing and dancing over at our place is far and away better than yours.'

Then Uenuku decided to have some sport. 'Let him down then,' he commanded, and Whakaturia was lowered, and everything happened as Tama had predicted. Whakaturia oiled his hair and put a huia feather in it, and tied a maro round his waist.

'Make a bright fire!' he said. 'Get rid of the smoke and have a good light so that you can all see me.' This was done, and taking the taiaha he had been given, Whakaturia stood up to dance. He began a rhythm with his feet which the people took up, clapping their hands together softly and humming a chant that fitted it. As the rhythm grew more exciting Whakaturia danced down one side of the house, holding back as yet, making only slow steps with his feet and small movements with the taiaha. His body was gleaming with oil, his hair was a shining black, and the white tip of the huia feather in his topknot quivered with the jerks he gave his head. He showed the whites of his eyes, and they glistened, like those other eyes of paua shell in the carved head of his taiaha. He moved along one side of the centre posts toward the door, and back along the other to the closed end of the house.

When all the people were gripped by the rhythm of his dance, which was in a style they had not seen before, Whakaturia suddenly cried: 'I'm hot! Just slide the door back a bit and give me some air, would you?' and then he took a little rest. 'Come on,' they said after a few moments, 'show us more.' For they were impatient now to see this dance that Whakaturia was working up to, and which had not yet really begun. So he stood up and began again. As he did so, he saw a movement just outside the door, and knew that his brother was ready with sticks to bolt up the door and window at the proper moment. And so he turned to the right, and stuck out his tongue as far as it would go and rolled his eyes, and made a hideous grimace in that direction. Then he turned to the left, and did the same to the people on that side, and with flourishes of his taiaha he went slowly into motion, with his eyes glaring, and the red tuft of feathers on his taiaha giving now and then a little shake, like a kingfisher killing a bird that hangs from its beak. The chant and the rhythm were growing in excitement, the voices of all the people were joined in a strange chill harmony, and all their minds were on the dance. Suddenly Whakaturia sprang about with a splendid leap that made them all catch their breath. With the bloodcurdling yells of a warlike haka, he stamped along the house on one side of the centre poles. He returned, and did the same along the other side for the benefit of the people there. Then, in an instant, and so quickly that no one realized what was happening, he leapt out through the door. Tama sprang forward and slid it shut and bolted it, and 'Turia took the other piece of wood and closed up the window. And there were the whole of Uenuku's tribe, locked up in their own great meeting house, cursing and chattering like a hole full of young parrots in a tree. Away ran Tama and his brother through the night to their own village. After a while, someone who was passing removed the bolts, and Uenuku's people all poured out, the whole thousand of them, in a very bad mood indeed.

Uenuku and Toi felt stupid and annoyed next day, to think that the two young sons of Houmai had not only stolen their breadfruit but also had escaped so easily after being caught. 'If we had had the sense to kill them straight away they would never have escaped like this,' said Toi. 'Some day that fellow Whakaturia is going to come back here and take utu for our having strung him up in the roof. That is, if we do not do something first.'

So Toi and Uenuku agreed to join forces and attack Houmai's

village. They gathered their warriors on their marae and inflamed their feelings with warlike speeches, and songs and chants. First, old Uenuku made a speech, then portly Toi, and other orators strode up and down the marae, speaking when they walked in one direction but always silent in the other, and coughing from time to time to indicate the gravity of their subject. When the two chiefs were satisfied that their men all shared their anger, they saw to it that all were armed—some with throwing spears, some with slings and river stones, some with taiaha and maipi, and all with patu or mere, short clubs for the in-fighting that was sure to follow. There were also men with kotaha, or throwing sticks, for throwing lighted darts on to the thatch of the roofs of Houmai's village.

When all were armed and ready the usual ceremony was conducted at the village latrine, with every warrior kneeling down to bite the crossbar with his teeth. This gives a feeling of protection against an enemy's secret powers. Then they all stripped themselves naked and stood in a stream in turns while a priest sprinkled water on them with a leafy branch, and made them tapu to the war-god, Tu. They had no dealings with their women then until the fight was over.

They marched on Houmai's village, a handpicked hokowhitu of one hundred and forty men, and found the people there preparing to fight them. Spears and stones, taunts and insults came from behind the palisades, and the tall figures of Tama te kapua and Whakaturia appeared, and jeered at Uenuku's men. Fairly soon some flaming darts from the attackers, tossed over the palisades, set fire to some of the village roofs, and this provoked a young warrior of Houmai's side, eager for honour in his first experience of war, to take too big a risk. When one of Uenuku's men rushed close to the pa to throw a torch, this man leapt down with a yell, armed only with a maipi. He swung it exultantly, for he hoped his man would be the 'first fish', or the first one to be killed. But it struck his opponent's shoulder, not his head, and a rush of Uenuku's men protected their own warrior, so that the man who leapt was

They saw to it that all were armed

slaughtered in a moment, to the jeers and laughter of the attackers, and *he* became the first fish. And now the fighting grew more savage, and a breach in Houmai's fortifications was forced, with the help of a heavy log, by a storming party of Uenuku's men.

To the surprise of the attacking chiefs, the voice of Houmai was now heard calling, 'Let them in! Let them in here to the very house of Houmai!' and some dozens of Toi's and Uenuku's men poured through the gap. Then from the houses out rushed Tama te kapua and Whakaturia with a reserve of men who had not been on the palisades, and surprised the invaders and slaughtered them, while the men on the palisades closed up the gap behind them. In this engagement inside the pa, Whakaturia was gravely wounded.

Now all this was more than Toi or even Uenuku had intended when they planned their raid, and next a horrible scene occurred. For Tama and their supporters were filled with blood-lust, and they cut up and cooked the bodies of some men of Uenuku's tribe who were their close relations, being descended as he was from Tamatea kai ariki. One young chief, they degraded utterly before his corpse was even cold. They cut off his head, and it rolled in the dust, and some children, screaming with excitement, rushed in and made a plaything of it, poking sticks in its ears, and holding it aloft on one of their teka darts. They gouged its eyes out, and one of the children, holding them up before his own eyes, rushed round screaming the name of the man to whom they had belonged, pretending to be him. But they soon grew tired of their game and left the head, and a dog came forward and took it, and carried it to a shady place. So that young chief perished, and all this time the captors were neatly butchering the remainder of the corpse in preparation for a feast. The rest of Toi's and Uenuku's force returned to their own lands with the sad news of their loss.

Now this was a very great crime that was committed in Houmai's village, to act in this fashion to men who were near relations; and Houmai became very thoughtful when he considered what had been done. Soon afterwards, Whakaturia died from his injuries, and Houmai knew that this was a punishment inflicted by the gods, who were offended. For Houmai knew that men must try to live in peace if they can. He therefore called his other sons to him, and their cousins who had acted with them, and he said to them:

'O my children, O Tama, O Tia, O Hei, listen to what I say. There was once but one great chief here in Hawaiki, and that was Whaka- tau, the son of Tuhuruhuru. Now you, who are building great canoes to sail to the distant land that Kupe found, go from here in peace together, and when you reach that land do not follow after Tu, the war-god. If you do you will perish, all of you, as surely as if the winds of Tawhiri were to sweep your canoes into the throat of Te Parata, the whirlpool from which no canoe returns. Go rather in peace and follow Rongo, the god of husbandry. It is war and its evils that are driving you from here. Then live by peace, not war, in the country where it is said there is land enough for all, and no one need go stealing food. Go there, and build up a great new people in your new land.'

Soon after this Houmai also died, and Tama te kapua determined that his tribe should become great in the new land that Kupe found. To this end he planned the building and provisioning of the great canoe Te Arawa.

Te Arawa is the canoe, Tama te kapua is the chief, and Ngatoro i rangi is the navigator. From the people of this canoe, the largest that came to New Zealand from Hawaiki, are descended the Arawa tribes.

THE VOYAGE OF THE ARAWA

IT was Hei and Tia and their helpers who built the canoe of Tama te kapua, which was named Te Arawa, the name of a kind of shark. At the same time other canoes were being built on Hawaiki, among them the Tainui, the Takitimu, the Tokomaru, and the Pukeatea wainui. They were smaller than the Arawa. The Arawa was a double canoe with a house built on it for shelter from the sun and rain. There are some who say the Arawa was not a double canoe but merely had a very large outrigger of sufficient size to allow this cabin to be built.

The Arawa and Tainui were got ready for launching at the same time of year. The adzes that hewed them out were Hauhau te rangi and Tutauru, the famous adzes that were made from Ngahue's greenstone, Pounamu. From that same stone came many precious ornaments, including the eardrop Kaukaumatua which belonged to Tama te kapua. These two canoes were leaving Hawaiki because of the terrible warfare that followed the stealing of Uenuku's breadfruit by Tama and his brother. Most of the people who travelled in them were Houmai's people, but in the Tainui canoe were some close relations of Uenuku.

At this time both of these canoes were tapu, since they had not been freed of the tapu that was placed on them while they were being built. When both were fitted out, and the stocks of dried kumara and shellfish, gourds of drinking water, birds and rats in cages, lines and hooks and fishing nets and seeds for planting in the new land—when all these things had been stowed on board, Tama te kapua still lacked a skilful tohunga to navigate. He therefore made himself agreeable to Ngatoro i rangi, the navigator of the Tainui, and asked him to come on board the Arawa to carry out certain religious rites that were needed before she could sail. Ngatoro's wife, Kearoa, was with him, and Tama said: 'Bring Kearoa too, so that she can desanctify the Arawa for us with an offering of seaweed.' For it was a custom that the first fish caught from a canoe—or if it was not a fishing-canoe, then seaweed in place of fish—must be offered to the gods for the protection of the males, and a second piece for the females; and so far this had not been done. Ngatoro agreed to this request and went on board with Kearoa for a trial run under sail. Since he was a priest he was given a place of honour in the house that stood on the kiato, or booms, which joined the Arawa's two sections. And away they sailed.

Now Tama saw to it that Ngatoro i rangi was properly entertained on board, and that his mind was taken off whatever might be happening. And the Arawa sped away before the wind, directly out to sea. At last Ngatoro looked out and saw that land was far behind. 'Shorten sail!' he cried. 'Slow down, or I'll miss Tainui.' For the Tainui also was to sail that afternoon, and Ngatoro had arranged that she should come alongside Te Arawa in open water and he would leap across. 'Oh, wait a little longer,' said Tama, looking astern at Tainui's sail. 'They will catch us up in a while.' But the Tainui's sail grew smaller and smaller as night came on. She dropped still further astern, and in the night all sight of her was lost. Thus Tama te kapua got Ngatoro i rangi as navigator for Te Arawa. He knew very well that Ngatoro could be relied on to set the proper course, since he wished to rejoin his friends at their common destination.

This was not the only trick of this sort that Tama te kapua played when Te Arawa sailed. He also managed to steal the wife of one of his crew, Ruaeo. Her name was Whakaoti rangi. She was installed on board with all her belongings and those of her husband, when at the last moment Tama said to him: 'Oh, Rua, just run

Eke, eke,
eke panuku,
Hui e—
Taiki e—

'She lifts, she lifts, she glides into safety! O Unity, O Victory!' they chanted. These words today are the anthem of those people.

So Ngatoro's chants, and the chant of all the Arawa people, raised the bow of that great canoe, and drew her back from the Throat of Te Parata. Much of their precious cargo, their food and animals, and some of their men and women were lost overboard in this dreadful storm, the punishment for Tama's acts. Of their dried kumara and shellfish a great deal had soon to be thrown away, and some of their rats and birds were drowned or died. Their chiefly dogs, being not tied up but free to find safe places for themselves, survived the storm. But Whakaoti rangi, the wife of Ruaeo, who was travelling alone with all her family goods, lost nearly all that she possessed. This is the reason for the saying, when there is not much food to give a visitor, 'It is the half-empty basket of Whakaoti rangi.' But they dried out the remainder of their food and apportioned it, and when the storm had passed they spent a day in fishing for ocean fish. And so, in the cooler winds of the latitudes into which Te Arawa had sailed, they completed their journey. They reached these islands in December, when all the pohutukawa is in bloom. They sailed in calm weather into the eastern end of the large bay we now call the Bay of Plenty. There they found the smaller bay in which they landed, and to which they shortly gave a name.

*   *   *

Now although the waters of these coasts, even in midsummer, were pale and chill compared with the waters of their homeland, and the colours of the land were mild, and the sky and the clouds were never so brilliant as those of Hawaiki, still the voyagers were astonished at what they saw as they guided Te Arawa into the bay.

For all along the shore, behind the beach and hanging from the rocks, were ranged the immense pohutukawa trees, each one a smother of rich red bloom. Never before had the eyes of those people seen such a mass of red, the sacred colour. As they glided in to the beach, Tauninihi, a young chief of the Arawa, carried away by the sight before him, took his chiefly headgear Taiwhakaea, which was made of scarlet feathers from the parrots of Hawaiki, and threw it into the bay. 'There'll be no shortage of kura in this land,' he cried. And then they beached the Arawa, and all leapt out to stretch their legs.

No sooner was Tauninihi ashore than he ran to gather armfuls of the kura. But he found it was nothing but flimsy flowers, which fell to pieces and were nothing the moment that he touched them. And so he regretted his foolish action, for his headgear had floated away by then. Later it was found on the beach at Mahiti by Mahina, one of the crew. Tauninihi asked him to give it up, but Mahina refused; he considered it his since Tauninihi had thrown it away. And hence the saying 'te kura pae a Mahina', Mahina's drifted kura, meaning 'finding is keeping'.

One of the first things they did after unloading the Arawa was to set up a tuaahu, or sacred place, to give thanks for their safe arrival and to house their gods; and the next was to dig a kumara patch and plant their seed. In the time of Governor Grey it was said the Arawa's kumara were still established there. And while this was being done, parties of people went off inland to look for food. Tired out from their arduous journey, the whole crew rested for some days at the spot where they landed, and only built themselves rough shelters to begin with. They then split up into parties to explore their new country, and one party shortly returned with the news that on a beach not far away was the fresh carcase of a stranded paraoa, or sperm whale.

Now it happened that the Tainui, which had not experienced the Arawa's delays, and which also had missed the fearful storm at the Throat of Te Parata, had already reached Aotearoa, and had landed further along on the same coast. And its people had already found this whale, and considered it to be theirs. They were not nearby when the Arawa people came upon it, but in due course the separate parties met, for they liked its putrid flesh, and valued the bones and teeth for ornaments and clubs. When they had recovered from the surprise of meeting, they unfortunately got into an argument about the ownership of the whale. Their chiefs came to the spot to hear the facts, and at last, on the suggestion of Ngatoro i rangi, who felt some loyalty to both canoes, they agreed to settle the matter by comparing the posts of the tuaahu that each party had set up on arriving, to see which one was the oldest. Since Tama te kapua had not yet forgotten his father's parting words about living in peace in the new land, this seemed the right course to take, so long as it showed the whale to belong to him.

But it was found that the posts of the Arawa tuaahu were still green and fresh, whereas those of the Tainui people looked old and brown. There are some who say that the Tainui people deliberately dried out their posts over a fire when they erected their tuaahu on arriving. The Tainui people also showed a piece of rope which they had tied to the jawbone of the whale, as a sign of their claiming it. So the whale was surrendered to the Tainui, and the Arawa people in consequence decided to make a new home somewhere else. Ever since that time, and because of the whale, the bay where the Arawa and Tainui landed has been known as Whangaparaoa, or Spermwhale bay.*

The main body of the Arawa people, under Taikehu, set off along the coast toward the west, while Tama te kapua, Ngatoro i rangi, and their families travelled in comfort with a picked crew in the Arawa, sailing at leisure and keeping in touch with the shore party at points along the way.

The shore party must have travelled inland for a while, since they missed encountering the people of the Pukeatea wainui, the

* West of Cape Runaway.

canoe that left Hawaiki after the Tainui and brought Ruaeo. It had landed at the little inlet now called Maketu, which both the Arawa and her shore party must have passed soon after setting out. Ruaeo would have liked to find his wife, Whakaoti rangi; but he did not find her yet.

After some days the Arawa and her shore party met at the entrance to a large and useful harbour, with a bigger expanse of sheltered water than those people from Hawaiki had ever seen. It gave both anchorage and fishing grounds, and hence the name it has today, Tauranga.

Standing up in the canoe when they had anchored there, the Arawa chiefs took part in the custom of appropriating land by naming it after parts of their bodies. First, Tama te kapua picked out the point now known as Maketu Heads and said: 'I name that place the Point of Tama te kapua's nose,' and it was his thenceforward without dispute, since no one would ever think of digging, or building a house, on Tama te kapua's nose. Hei then pointed to Otawa and said: 'I name that place the Abdomen of Waitahanui a Hei,' and thus it became the property of his son, Waitahanui. And Tia pointed to the place now known as Rangiuru and said: 'I name that place the Abdomen of Tapuika a Tia,' and it became the property of his son, Tapuika.

The Arawa then went out to the island that lies five miles off shore near there. Not a stick of firewood could they find when they landed, and so, remembering the saying from Hawaiki, 'I suppose you're at Motiti, as there is no firewood,' they called the island Motiti. They hauled the Arawa ashore and painted her with ochre and shark-oil, and they set up their tuaahu.

By this time Ruaeo, at Maketu, had heard that Tama te kapua's people were in the vicinity. When he learned that the Arawa was only across at Motiti, he took a fishing line and went down to the shore by night. After saying certain powerful karakia over his line and its sinker, he swung it round his head and cast it over to Motiti. Its hooks caught on the Arawa, and while her crew and chiefs were

So the whale was surrendered to the Tainui ➤

fast asleep on board he hauled the great canoe to Maketu, where he had one hundred and forty men waiting to help him deal with Tama te kapua. Ruaeo drew the Arawa on shore, sat down under her side, and played a tune on his putorino, a little flute-like instrument made of hollow wood. His wife, Whakaoti rangi, who was sleeping on board with Tama te kapua, woke up and recognised her husband's playing. She came out on to the beach, and she and Ruaeo passed the night together. In due course Ruaeo said to her: 'Now you go back to your new husband and I will play my putorino again so that he can hear as well. Then you can say you had a dream about me. That will make him jealous and he'll hit you, and you can leave him in a rage and come to me again.'

So Whakaoti rangi did all this, and Tama te kapua struck her, and she left him. Then Ruaeo said a rotu which put everyone in the canoe into a deep sleep. And late in the morning, when the sun was well up in the sky, he gave the Arawa's side a smart blow with his patu. She resounded like a drum, the people in her all woke up, and were dazzled by the morning sun. When a few looked over the side they saw Ruaeo's hokowhitu, twice seventy men, all sitting on the beach below them, decked out in so many white feathers, it looked as if they had been living on the gannet island of Karewa.

It would have been an easy slaying for Ruaeo. His hundred and forty men in that moment had the whole Ngati Arawa at their mercy. But this is what Ruaeo said: 'Come out here, Tama te kapua! Let us fight this out alone! If you are stronger than I, well and good. If I am stronger than you, I'll crush your body in the sand. And he placed in the shade beneath the Arawa's hull something he had been holding in his hand, a little woven basket with something in it.

Up stood the huge figure of Tama te kapua, and all of his people and Ruaeo's men watched to see what would happen next. For both these men were giants. Tama te kapua was nine feet tall, and Ruaeo was two feet taller than that. Ruaeo stood back and allowed the man who stole his wife to jump from the beached canoe. A space was cleared, and with Tama's people watching from the Arawa, and Ruaeo's supporters ranged up facing them, the two huge men prepared to fight it out.

Tama te kapua had a taiaha whose hilt was decked with scarlet feathers. Ruaeo held a similar weapon, and these taiaha, like the men who wielded them, were of great weight and enormous strength. The two men began with some footwork in the sand, and with eyes glaring they sidled about one another, feeling their way toward the first clash of weapons. Their separate parties of supporters held their breath. The first fierce blow was struck by Tama. But Rua parried it, it glanced off the club end of his taiaha without so much as touching him. Seeing Tama slightly off his balance, Rua, to everyone's surprise, then suddenly threw his weapon down and swiftly seized his opponent by the wrists. With his powerful hands he rendered Tama's weapon useless, and with his greater height and equal strength he soon had his enemy on the sand. Tama half rose, but Rua forced him down again, and edged him toward the side of his canoe, under the very eyes of his companions. Their taiaha had now been pulled away by spectators, and a fierce wrestling match was in progress. Then Rua, in a second when one hand was free, snatched up the flaxen kit that he had put beneath the Arawa. It was filled with verminous lice which he had been collecting for this occasion from the heads of his companions. He squeezed it open and swiftly rubbed the crawling lice on Tama's head and in his ears and eyes. Thus Ruaeo heaped insult and shame, as well as maddening irritation, on Tama te kapua. He was then content. While his enemy tried frantically to clear his face and head, Ruaeo stood back to get his breath. He rubbed his own hands clean in the sand and flicked the sweat from his body. His nostrils were flaring as he breathed, and he said contemptuously to Tama: 'There, I've beaten you now! You can keep the woman. Perhaps she'll rid you of your filthy lice.' But Tama te kapua, although his family and his fellow chiefs heard well enough, could scarcely hear these words, for scratching and rubbing his head and gasping with the maddening itch the vermin caused.

Then Ruaeo and his hundred and forty men departed, to settle in some other place. Where they went to is not known, there are no tribes today that claim descent from the Pukeatea wainui, and some declare no such canoe existed. The woman, Whakaoti rangi, they left behind for Tama.

So it was that the descendants of Houmai tawhiti learned that his words concerning peace could not easily be fulfilled in their new and uninhabited land. For quarrelling, like vermin, travelled with them, and evils done on Hawaiki's shores bred evil here.

After this Tama te kapua became involved in a quarrel with Kahu mata momoe, and because of it he and Ngatoro left Maketu and Motiti and moved on up the coast. They left the Arawa drawn up on dry land at Maketu, in the care of Hei and Tia who had built her.

For a time they stayed at Tauranga, where Taikehu was living and the fishing was good. There are some who say that Tama became ill at this time; for when he was staying at an inlet at the northern end of Tauranga harbour, all his companions ate well, but Tama only nibbled, katikati, at his food. And from this the place became known as Katikati o Tama te kapua. Today we call it Katikati. Then Whakahau was so named because Tama took shelter there but ate no food, and so they went on to Whitianga, so named from their crossing the river there, and finally to sleep at Moehau, where in later years Tama te kapua died, and was buried.

*   *   *

Now the people of the Arawa canoe made many explorations inland from their various coastal settlements, and the most marvellous journeys were those of the priest, Ngatoro i rangi. When Ngatoro went about the country, wherever he found dry valleys he stamped on the earth and made springs flow.

Ihenga also made discoveries inland. It was he who found the lakes near Rotorua, and he did so in this way. Soon after the Arawa

Ngatoro stamped on the earth to make water flow

landed it was found that there lived in the bush some dark brown
birds which had strong legs but no wings. These birds, which the
people called kiwi from their cry, remained hidden by day and
only came out to feed at night, when they dug out grubs and

Kiwi

worms with their long and slender beaks. Their feathers, it was
found, made handsome cloaks for chiefs, and they were also food.
Because they only went abroad by night they could not be hunted
like other birds. But since they had no wings, but could only run,
they could be caught by the chiefly dogs that had been brought
from Hawaiki.

Ihenga went with his two dogs one night to catch some kiwi. He
went by way of Kakomiti to Paritangi, and one of his dogs, chasing
a kiwi, ran after it into a lake. There the dog ate some fish and
shellfish, and after it had returned to Ihenga with the kiwi in its
mouth, it shook water all over him. Then it vomited up the raw
fish and shellfish it had eaten. In this way Ihenga knew there must

be a roto, or lake, nearby, and he discovered Rotoiti, little lake, and left a mark there to claim it for himself. He went on to find Rotorua and marked that as his own, but as he went round one side of it he saw signs of occupation. Without showing himself to the people there he considered how he might dispossess them. In the bush he looked for a suitable spot for a tuaahu, and another place where nets could be hung up to dry. Having found them, he collected mossy stones to make the tuaahu, and old pieces of sea-weed that looked as if they had been used for offerings long before. In a thick growth of bush he arranged the stones and posts of his tuaahu and tied bundles of dried flax to them. When it all looked old and used he went to the settlement, which was the home of Maru punganui.

They saw him coming and called out, 'A stranger, a stranger!' He sat down where he was, so that they had to approach him, and when they did so he jumped up, and without waiting for them to begin their speeches he shouted at them: 'What theft is this? Who are you people, that you occupy my land?' For he could see now that they had nets hung out on rails to dry, and whata stacked with dried fish and fern-root. Ihenga turned on them in a rage, his throat growing larger as he spoke, and demanded to be told who said that they could live there. 'Go away!' he cried, 'leave this land to the man it belongs to, and who has owned it for a very long time.'

Then Maru punganui, who was the son of Tu a Rotorua, and a very mild person, said to the stranger 'But this is not your place, Ihenga, it belongs to me. Look at my village here, and my cultiva-tions and my tuaahu. Where are yours?' 'Come with me and see them,' said Ihenga. So they went, and climbed the hill some distance. 'Look,' said Ihenga, 'there is my net hanging against the rocks.' And so it appeared. But it was only a mark like a net hang-ing up, caused by a slip. 'There are the posts around my village,' he said. But it was only the stumps of some old dead trees. 'Now come and see my sacred place,' he said, and Maru punganui went with Ihenga to the thing he had made in the bush. He was very frightened of Ihenga's manner, and he believed him, and gave up possession of all that land and the lake, and went away. But some of his descendants, under the chiefs Kawaarero and Mataaho, occupied the island Mokoia, in the middle of the lake.

*　　*　　*

At this time Ngatoro was performing his wondrous acts further inland to the south. He went round stamping on the earth to make water flow, and then he came out on the great central plains and found Lake Taupo, the lake so large that it was called Te Moana, the Sea. Here Ngatoro walked by the shore, and threw his staff into the lake, where it took root and became a giant totara tree. In the time of Governor Grey it was still to be seen there, standing up in the waters of the lake. Ngatoro also shook out his tihe, his travelling cloak and sleeping mat, on various occasions. While he was beside the lake he shook it over the water, and from the bits that fell there sprang the inanga, the little innumerable fishes with silver bellies in which the lake abounds. Then, when he was travelling through the rough country beyond the lake, a part of his cloak was torn off by the undergrowth, and the shreds took root and became painanga trees, as tall as white pines.

Whenever Ngatoro climbed a hill he left marks to claim his ownership, and these marks became patupaiarehe, the little people or evil spirits who live there still, in places remote from men. It is these patupaiarehe who are offended if anyone takes embers from a cooking fire and uses them to start the fire inside a sleeping house. If this be done, however many people there may be sleeping in the house with the fires burning, the patupaiarehe will come and press them to death in their sleep. Sometimes all of the people in a house have been pressed to death in this way, even though the door and the window were closed. Ngatoro's patupaiarehe have caused it to happen because the burning charcoal was taken from a cooking fire.

When he had rested by the shores of Taupo, Ngatoro saw the summit of mount Tongariro, and it was dazzling white, as white as the surf of the breakers on the beach at Whangaparaoa. He told his party, when leaving them at the camp below, that on no account should any of them eat food until he returned, and he began to climb the mountain. He found that the whiteness there was not like the surf but was extremely cold, and after a time it hurt his feet. He had not quite reached the summit when those he had left behind, becoming hungry, disobeyed him and ate food. For this reason he found the greatest difficulty in climbing, and was nearly frozen to death. But by his enchantments Ngatoro saved himself. He stood there on the snow and shouted karakia to the gods of Hawaiki to send him fire, to warm him. They heard, and Ruaumoko sent fire from his place beneath of the bosom of Papa tu a nuku. The fire came from beneath Hawaiki, it travelled under the sea like a whale. As it drew near this land it rose to the surface and spouted, and this made that sulphurous and smoking island in the Bay of Plenty, Whakaari.* Then it came under the land by way of Mautohora, Okakaru, Rotoehu and Rotorua, Whakarewarewa, Tarawera, Orakei Korako and Wairakei, spouting up at all these places and making geysers, boiling mud-pools, steam-pits, and hot clear streams that flow beside cold mountain streams. When it reached Ngatoro it stopped, and it turned three mountains, Tongariro, Ngauruhoe, and Ruapehu, into volcanoes. So Ngatoro was given warmth, and when he felt revived he descended, and returned to Maketu, where Tama te kapua at that time was still living.

When Tama went up the coast to live at Moehau, Ngatoro went over to live on the island of Motiti, leaving only Hei and Tia at Maketu.

*   *   *

Now during all this time the people of the Tainui canoe had been absent from this part of the country. The Tainui, under its chief Hoturoa, with Rakataura as priest, left Whangaparaoa shortly

* White Island.

after the Arawa itself, and sailed across the Bay of Plenty with all her people aboard and no party on the shore. They went up round the Moehau peninsula* and into the gulf it encloses.† Then Hoturoa sailed northwards and they saw Rakau mangamanga,‡ and the little rocky islet that lies off it, Motu kokako, which is pierced by a hole that canoes can paddle through. They went as far as Muri whenua,§ and finding that the land ended there, they returned down the same coast into the gulf again, and so to Tamaki.

As they were coming down this coast Marama kikohura, one of their women of chiefly rank, expressed a wish to go ashore for a time. She said she would walk overland and meet them further on, and so she was put ashore with some provisions, and a slave to accompany her. In due course she rejoined the canoe, and eventually they all went ashore at Tamaki, which is still known by that name. They went up to the head of the creek and noticed that further inland, as they thought, there were flocks of seagulls and oyster-catchers. They investigated, and found that only a short distance away, separated from their creek by low ground, was a vast, pale, blue-grey harbour which emptied itself of water every day and became nothing but mudflats, braided by frothy creeks that returned each day by the way they had gone. Around the edges of this place were many mangrove trees, all standing in the mud. When they had marvelled at this mournful scenery and the strange behaviour of the harbour, Hoturoa decided to haul the Tainui over the portage. This was done, and to that place they gave the name Otahuhu. The harbour they crossed over into is nowadays called the Manukau.

The first canoe to be hauled across was the Tokomaru. The Tokomaru and her people were with the Tainui. They got the Tokomaru over without any difficulty, but when they tried to haul Tainui across she became firmly stuck, and would not move. Chants were sung, such as make heavy weights light and remove

* Coromandel.   † Hauraki Gulf.   ‡ Cape Brett.   § North Cape.

The fire turned three mountains into volcanoes

obstacles, but without result. Then Marama, the woman who had walked on shore when they were up the coast, stood by the bow of the canoe and sang the chant that begins

Toia Tainui,
tapatu ki te moana . . .

In the course of this chant she gave away the fact that when she and her slave were ashore together they had misbehaved. This confession loosened Tainui, she began to slide forward easily, and both canoes were run into the waters on the other side when the tide was high. Now Marama is the name for the moon. Some say it was the moon who assisted that dragging, with her tides.

They paddled down the harbour and found the rough and turbulent opening to the western sea, and passed out through it. Since they knew that to the northward the land came to an end, they turned to the south, and coasting along they passed the harbour where Aotea landed, and found the harbour further down which Turi had already named Kawhia. There they settled, and their people went inland in parties to discover the country.

One of Tainui's chiefs, Raumati, who was a relative of Uenuku in Hawaiki, went overland toward the east, where he learned how fortunate the Arawa people had been and how much of the country they had taken for their own. His party talked to the people whom they met, and he heard of Ngatoro's marvellous journey to the mountains, of the fire beneath the land, and the warm pools and boiling mud pools, and of the steam ovens that never needed fire, being kept on the boil by Ruaumoko below. Raumati saw that the people on this side had better and safer harbours than his people had found on the west, and he realised that this country was different from Hawaiki, for the lee-side was on the east and the weather side was west. Thus Raumati of Uenuku's clan grew jealous of the good fortune of the descendants of Houmai tawhiti.

Raumati and his party reached Tauranga, and there heard news of Tama te kapua and Ngatoro i rangi. He heard also that the Arawa was drawn up on the land at Maketu. And so he went to Maketu.

Now at this time none of its people were guarding the Arawa. They believed that all who were in the district were their friends. Hei and Tia, who built her, were still living at Maketu, but at this time, because it was a season of abundant food, they and their people were scattered along the coast or inland—fishing, snaring birds, collecting berries and gathering other food. Raumati did not know this when he reached the place. He approached with care, arriving in the evening, and halted on the river bank just opposite to where the Arawa was laid.

That great and beautiful canoe, built in Hawaiki by Hei and Tia and decorated with splendid carvings by the finest artists of the homeland, was drawn up into a space that had been cut for her among the trees. She was well protected by a gable roof, strongly built and thickly thatched with raupo reeds. Her handsome stern-piece could be seen at the near end of her house, her paint was fresh, and it was plain to Raumati that this magnificent canoe was not neglected by her owners.

When night came on, Raumati made a teka, or dart, and gave it a binding of tinder-dry materials at its point. When he had larded this with bird-fat he set it alight, and with a throwing stick he flung it across the river, saying a karakia that would ensure that it found its mark. It fell into the dry thatch of the Arawa's house, and stuck there. The roof caught fire, and soon it was all ablaze. The burning parts collapsed through the rafters and on to the Arawa, and while Raumati and his party watched from across the river, the Arawa was utterly destroyed, in a blaze whose glow was seen in the sky for miles around. Towards the dawn, since there appeared to be none of the Arawa people there, Raumati crossed the river. He found that the pa of Maketu was quite empty, no one at all was there. Then, with his party, he went away from that place.

On the night when the Arawa burned, those of her people who

in the house, and set up a sound of mournful wailing that affected the feelings of everyone who heard it. Amongst these ladies, wailing very loudly, was that Whakaoti rangi whom Tama carried off from Ruaeo when the Arawa left the homeland; and certain other wives of his, and women also who had never liked him. They cut their foreheads and their chests with shells and pieces of obsidian, that tears and blood might dry together on their bodies and marks be left for ever to show their grief. They wore green plaited wreaths about their heads of kawakawa leaves, and Tama's wives wore little caps of dark black seaweed. These wives all fasted while they mourned, and cut their hair short. Only in the night, when they were very hungry and no one was to see, did they secretly accept small offerings of food. And Tama's principal wife went away and hanged herself with rope.

While the body of that chief still lay on the mat on which he died the people of the village came in procession to pay their homage. An elder led them, they slowly filed toward the house, and in front of it he stopped and said these words to the one within: 'Farewell, O sir! Depart to the world of night, never to return!'

The women stood behind him wailing a pihe, a dirge with ancient words that is always sung, with waving hands and twining of the fingers. The tears rolled down their cheeks, and mucus dribbled from their nostrils, since that is correct; and after their leader had made a formal speech they filed inside the whare mate, and all pressed their noses, each one for a very long time, against the noses of the mourners of the family. After this these women of the village went out to start preparing food for all the visitors who were arriving from other parts, and the principal mourners prepared the body to be seen by them. Before the joints of Tama had gone stiff they trussed his body up, in the sitting position. 'The tying, the tying, the binding, the binding, who is able to do it? . . .' that was the chant they used as they passed the cord around his knees and his neck. They oiled his hair and dressed it with feathers, they painted his face all red with ochre to show his rank, from his ears they hung white pompoms of the down of albatross, and on his shoulders they placed a dogskin cloak—a cloak that Tama te kapua had brought to this country from Hawaiki. His greenstone ornament they hung from his neck, and they put his patu and his taiaha in his hands.

While the women were attending to these things the sacred spade was made for Tama's burial. The men who watched the making of this kaheru chanted these words that speak of Tama's o matenga, his food for the journey to the dead:

> Closed up, closed up,
> in the womb of night.
> With the early dawn
> eat the offering of the dead,
> from the cultivation of your father
> which is left in the world.

> Closed up, closed up!
> In early dawn
> eat the spirit of the fat,
> the spirit of the taro.
> Your food to feed you is the sandfly.
> Eat it in Pairau, your abode.

Soon the visitors began to arrive in groups from other parts, all bearing gifts. Some bore coverings for the body of the chief, some bore food as offerings to the feast. They brought fine mats, dress cloaks, and ornaments, and as they approached the village, the women with the shrillest voices greeted them in these words: 'Haeremai ki o tatou mate e!'—'Come to our dead.' And so the tangihanga of Tama te kapua began. The arriving chiefs cried brief farewells to him from the marae, and their women wailed in answer to the wailing of the family mourners. They all lined up along the marae, with the gifts spread out in the space between, and the tangi went on many hours, until Ngatoro i rangi stood up and said: 'Enough.' Then all sat down to rest, and settled themselves to listen to the speeches of the old grey-headed men, the visiting chiefs. These men wore wreaths of kawakawa, like their women, and they spoke in grave and sorrowing tones, with many learned references to the gods, to their ancestors in the homeland across the sea, and to the honour of their tribe which Tama te kapua had founded in the new land. It was correct that every speaker should address the dead chief first, and they did so:

'Go! Go to the other world!
Go to your ancestors, O Tama te kapua!
Go to the tribe!

Travel along the path of the hundreds,
travel along the path of the thousands,
go by the path from which no messenger returns!'

These words were said by a chief who had come from Maketu with Ngatoro, and he spoke of the greatness of the man they mourned and compared him in greatness with their lost canoe, Te Arawa, by whose strong timbers and enduring sail they all had been carried from Hawaiki. When they had said sufficient of the dead these speakers lifted their faces and cried out, 'Karanga, Karanga, Karanga!' They thereby changed the subject to the living, to the tribe that remained and the relatives who mourned. When the final speaker sang an old lament, the people knew that this part of the proceedings was concluded.

Then all the visitors lined up and all their hosts lined up, and the hongi was made between them. For a very long time the visitors filed slowly past the hosts, all the men and all the women, and many young people who were not born in Hawaiki but in this land; and all pressed their noses together in salutation and friendship. In this way all the visitors were introduced, and the depth of their sympathy was made known. Afterwards, all the gifts were taken to the house where the body sat, and were laid before it,

The tangihanga of Tama te kapua

while two small children sat with woven fans to flick away the flies, lest these be evil spirits in disguise. When all these ceremonies were completed the company were entertained to a very great feast, which meal included the baked flesh of the bodies of two slaves. And in the evening there was singing and dancing in the meeting-house.

After some days, when the last of the expected visitors had arrived and it was time to bury him, the body of Tama te kapua was taken from the whare mate. With solemn chants to Tu and Rongo, gods of war and husbandry, those who were carrying the corpse walked slowly from the marae and led the long procession to the stream. They stopped there, and a pole was stuck in the water for the dead, and Ngatoro i rangi said this karakia that is always used on such occasions:

> Plant food for the night,
> the great night,
> the long night,
> the dark night,
> the night to be touched,
> the night to be felt,
> the night not seen,
> the night to be followed.
> Plant the pole. It stands—
> the pole of Tane rua nuku,
> the pole of night is planted.
> This is all for the night!
> For the dead this pole!

Then another pole was set up for the living, and Ngatoro i rangi said this karakia:

> Plant food for the day,
> the world of light,
> the great day,
> the long day,
> the gloomy day,
> the clouded day,
> the swelling day.

Now plant the pole, it stands—
the pole of Tane,
the pole of the Tail of Heaven,
the pole of following day,
the pole of day is planted.
This is all for the day!
For the living this pole!

They then splashed through the cleansing water and followed to
the burying place, and the grave of Tama te kapua was dug there
with the sacred kaheru, and his body placed in it, and the kaheru
was burned. And that burial place was then intensely tapu, and no
person could ever go there. If he did so, he was killed. It remained
thus until two summers later, when the bones of Tama te kapua
were lifted, and were painted red with ochre, and put in another
sacred place.

And so they returned to the village, and food was cooked and
placed on all the things that had belonged to Tama te kapua. This
made them common, it desanctified them so they could be given
to the relatives and not be burnt. Thus all their obligations to their
chief were carried out, and the people's feelings were relieved, and
they turned to the enjoyment of food and dancing and songs; as
indeed they had already done by night, before their chief was
buried. In the meeting house at evening, the visitors and their
hosts competed in putting on their best performances, and the
young people were happy, and the elders slept, and sometimes
they woke and made speeches, and slept again.

Now after Tama te kapua had been buried by his people and
everything was properly attended to, his spirit set forth on its
journey to the country called Te Reinga, which is in the realm of
Hine nui te Po, Great Hine the Night. The road it was to take lay
northward from Moehau, to the northernmost tip of this island,
now called Cape Reinga. That is where all the spirits of men,
chiefs and commoners alike, leap off for the world below, where

their food is the bodies of sandflies, and no cooked food is ever eaten by them. This place from which they leave is called Te Rerengawairua, spirits' leaping-place.

The wairua of Tama te kapua crossed over the gulf from Moehau to the land that leads to Cape Reinga, it went on northwards until it came to the long flat beach on the western coast. It carried its token of its earthly home, a spray of seaweed from the coast near Moehau, and when it passed along the beach to the north of Ahipara, the spirit of the chief put down this spray on the lonely hill called Te Arai. It journeyed on toward the north and climbed that hill the dirges speak of, called the Summit of Haumu. Up there it paused, for from that hilltop can be seen the sea toward the east, the Great Ocean of Kiwa that Tama crossed when he was living, and also the sea toward the west, toward the night and death. The spirit paused there, it turned to look its last upon the land behind, and then descended to the stream called Wai o raro Po— Water of the Underworld. It crossed that stream and walked along the little beach called Te Oneirehia, Sand of Pleasure; and then it crossed another stream that runs down steeply from a rocky place and is called from the sound it makes Te Waingunguru, the Waters of Lamentation. At last the spirit of Tama te kapua reached the leaping-place, it sprang down the steep cliff face to where the pohutukawa tree called Akakite reinga sends down its twisted root toward the underworld. When it slithered down this root, the waves swept back the kelp that covers the entrance there, and it leapt in, and was gone, before the waves returned.

While he was dying, Tama te kapua told Ngatoro i rangi where he had hidden the precious eardrop Kaukaumatua, which was made from Ngahue's piece of greenstone, Pounamu. It was under the window of his former house at Maketu. He also told his children that they must return to Maketu and their relations there, and they did so. If they had not returned to Maketu that place would not have been left to them as a possession. They went there with

Ngatoro. As soon as he arrived, that priest went into the water to bathe himself and be made free of the tapu that was on him since his burying of Tama te kapua.

Ngatoro then took the daughter of Ihenga to wife, and he searched for the eardrop Kaukaumatua, and found it as Tama te kapua told him. After this the wife of Kahu mata momoe conceived a child.

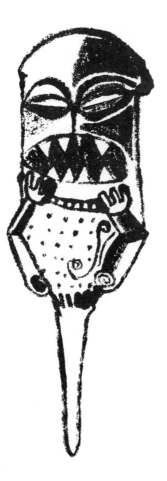

Kuiwai, a sister of Ngatoro i rangi, was wife of Manaia, a chief in Hawaiki. When Manaia cursed her brother she crossed the sea by magic to inform him, and Ngatoro travelled to Hawaiki for revenge. In return Manaia came to New Zealand, but the priest destroyed him and all his men.

THE AVENGING
OF MANAIA'S CURSE

NGATORO i rangi had two sisters in Hawaiki. Their names were Kuiwai and Haungaroa, and Kuiwai was one of the wives of a powerful chief, Manaia. After the canoes had left the homeland for Aotearoa, Manaia was obliged to hold a very great gathering and feast for the ceremonial cutting of his young son's hair. Large quantities of food were gathered and prepared for the visitors, and Kuiwai put food in her oven like all the other women. But when the ovens were opened after the ceremonies she found that her food was much underdone. The stones in her umu were not even properly hot. She was flustered and upset, and when she put the food before him Manaia flew into a rage. He beat her and he cursed her. She was used to that, but he cursed her brother too. 'Is the firewood as sacred as your brother's bones, that you cannot use enough?' he shouted, in a voice so loud that everyone could hear. 'Your stones are nowhere near the proper heat. If you do this to me again, I'll cook that brother of yours and show you how. I'll make him frizzle on the stones of Waikorora.'

Poor Kuiwai was overcome. What with the failure of her cooking, and her husband's horrible behaviour, it was all she could do to take out the remaining things and hand them round. She ate nothing herself, but went away to cry, and hid in the sleeping-house. Her sister Haungaroa tried to console her, but Kuiwai was too upset. She kept repeating the dreadful words her husband used. 'He asked me if the logs were as sacred as Ngatoro's bones,' she sobbed. 'He said my oven-stones must be my brother's kidneys if I couldn't make them hot! And then he said "*I'll* make him frizzle on red-hot stones from Waikorora".' Toward evening, Kuiwai dried her eyes and changed into a new skirt. It was made of fresh young shoots of toetoe, and she felt much better when she had put it on. Then she took out her gods, Kahukura, Itapawa and Rongomai, and uttered certain chants in front of them. The appearance of the gods was very favourable, so she said to Haungaroa: 'We shall go.' Then she wrapped up the gods and put them away, and made her preparations to depart.

It was the season of the favourable wind, Pungawere. That night the sisters took the gods, and also Maru and Te Iho o te rangi, The Heart of Heaven; and they had three other women as companions. These five set forth, to journey to the new land where Ngatoro was. They had no canoe, but were carried by their gods, who set them down on the burning island, Whakaari. When daylight came they floated on the sea once more and landed on this island, Aotearoa, at Tawhiuwhiu. Then they went inland to look for Ngatoro i rangi. On coming to a place which had a good view over the inland plain, they stopped to eat their food.

Now Haungaroa was very hungry after the journey, and when the rest had finished she went on eating, and still went on. This caused two of the ladies who had come with them to make remarks. 'What a long time you are taking, Haungaroa,' they said. Their comments gave annoyance, and Haungaroa slapped them in the face. They ran away and she chased them, and since they refused to come back she changed them into ti whanake, or cabbage trees, and they are still there today—two cabbage trees that stand on the shimmering plain in the heat of summer, but always move away when travellers approach. These trees have never yet been reached by any man.

The place where those women stopped to eat was called

13

Two cabbage trees that stand on the shimmering plain

Kaingaroa a Haungaroa, Haungaroa's long meal. The plain they looked out over is the Kaingaroa plain.

The sisters and their one remaining attendant travelled on till they came to the summit of a hill. While they sat down to rest, Haungaroa started thinking about her mother. This made her cry, she wept aloud, and that place has ever since been called Te Tangihanga, the Weeping-place. They continued their journey, and came to the summit of another hill, which they named Piopio. From there they could see the waters of Rotorua, blue and pleasant after the barren country they had been crossing. So they went down there and around the lake, and headed for Maketu. After this roundabout journey they asked some people near Tuhoro, on the coast, where Ngatoro i rangi lived. 'He lives up near that whata,' the people said, pointing to a storehouse on a hill. So the sisters went there, and came to Ngatoro's stockade. Lest anyone should think she was a common person, Kuiwai did not use the entrance gate but climbed straight over the palisade, and went immediately to the tapu place where Ngatoro usually sat. And there, to the astonishment and alarm of the people near-by, she herself sat down. The people ran off at once to tell Ngatoro, who was attending to his cultivations. 'There is a stranger just arrived,' they said. 'She has a dusty travelling bundle and looks as if she has come from a long way off. She did not use the gate, she climbed straight over the pa and then sat down in the place that is tapu to your sacred person.'

'I know who that will be,' said Ngatoro. 'Where is Te Kehu?'

'He is away at his kumara plot,' the messenger said.

'Then fetch him at once,' said Ngatoro, and when Te Kehu came, he and Ngatoro went to Ngatoro's house, and there the two sisters were. He asked them: 'Is that you?' They answered, 'Yes,' and he asked them what they sought. 'We have come,' said Kuiwai. And she undid her bundle and unwrapped the gods she had brought with her from Hawaiki, and gave them to her brother. These were the first gods for human beings that were brought to Aotearoa.

When the canoes came here they brought only the gods for kumara and fish.

After they had greeted one another with lamentations, Kuiwai said to Ngatoro: 'You have asked me why we have come. We must all go at once to the water and have the whakahoro performed over us. For you have been cursed, Ngatoro—by Manaia!'

This news was a dreadful shock to everybody present. Even Ngatoro was stunned for a moment, and others began to wail, and shriek, and stamp on the ground. Then all of them, without awaiting further details, rushed down to the stream and took off their clothes, and stood in the water while the chants of the whakahoro were said, to remove the horrible defilement. Then the priests went off and dug a long deep pit to bury the spirits of their enemies. They fetched some large flat shells that were kept for this purpose, and when these were used to push the earth back into the pit it scraped the enemy spirits in as well. The priests pressed down the earth, and trampled it with their feet, and covered it over with sacred mats. And all these things were done to the accompaniment of chants that made them effective. When the ceremonies were over, food was spread before the visitors and the hosts retired. After the guests had eaten, the company gathered in the meeting-house to hear about the curse. Ngatoro wept over Kuiwai, by way of welcoming her to this land, and then the old men of the place got up and made their speeches, and asked what had brought the sisters to their marae.

'A curse that Manaia uttered against you all,' said Kuiwai. She then described the scene at Manaia's purenga ceremony. All ears were turned to hear what the words of the curse had been. 'When everyone was ready for the feast,' said Kuiwai, 'we women opened our ovens, and the food in Kuiwai's oven was not well cooked. Some evil spirit cooled the stones. Manaia became enraged with Kuiwai, and cursed both her and you. He used the most terrible of curses. He said: "Is the firewood as sacred and precious as the bones of your brother, that you will not burn enough to heat the stones?"

And he said: "For this, I'll make your brother frizzle on red-hot stones from Waikorora." That curse is what has brought me here.'

There was an awful silence, as Kuiwai spread her cloak and squatted down. Then Ngatoro stood up. His eyes were glaring and his hands were clenched. For a long moment he said nothing. He gathered his cloak of kiwi feathers about his hips, and coughed a little. His people knew that his anger was immense. 'Then shall it be done to you, Manaia,' he said when at last he spoke. 'It is you whose bones shall be as firewood,' he said in a rising voice. 'And your flesh shall be cooked, with stones that come from Maketu!'

They waited to hear what Ngatoro would say to them next. After he had walked about a little he told them in a calm voice that in the morning they must all go out and find a very great totara tree, a totara with a straight clean trunk, ten lengths of a stretched-out man from its base to the first of its branches. All knew what he meant by this, they knew he had decided to return to Hawaiki and avenge Manaia's curse. For since the burning of the Arawa, those people had no voyaging canoe. They now must build one for Ngatoro, at once.

Early next morning they formed themselves in parties and all went off in various directions, Kuiwai among them. And she it was, the sister of Ngatoro and Manaia's former wife, who found a tree of the kind they needed—fallen down and half-buried in the ground. This tree was not rotted, it was good, its timber was already seasoned and ready to be worked. There was no need to bury it for a year; this had been done. So they dug it up and hollowed it and shaped the hull of a voyaging canoe, of sufficient size to take twice seventy warriors across the sea. And the name they gave it was Totarakeria—the totara dug up. They hauled it to the shore and provisioned it, and very shortly, with a hoko-whitu of one hundred and forty of his bravest warriors, Ngatoro i rangi set his course toward the homeland. This being the season of Pungawere, they reached Hawaiki at the end of seven days.

They landed at the place called Tara i whenua, under cover of

themselves down in dreadful attitudes among the ovens and actually in them, some with their mouths open and their heads thrown back, some apparently transfixed by spears stuck through to the ground, some sprawled across the bodies of their friends—and all prepared to lie like that until they were discovered, as they would be very soon. Their spears and taiaha, their maipi and their shorter clubs, they mostly concealed beneath their bodies. Ngatoro himself lay like an offering in the very tuaahu of his enemies, most horribly dead. But his fellow priests, the only ones not feigning dead, lay hidden in the undergrowth, to watch Manaia's priests arrive and choose the moment for attack. And so they waited for the dawn, with the blood drying out and turning black.

At the first light of day Manaia's priests came out to perform their usual rites. The sight that met their eyes astounded them. They turned and ran back shouting to the village: 'They have come! They have come, and they're all dead! There are hundreds of Ngatoro's men lying heaped up in our ovens, all freshly dead. We have only to cut them up and light the fires!'

Their cries aroused Manaia, who came at once. Even that chief was amazed at what he saw. 'This is the fulfilment of my prayer,' he said to the people gathered round him. 'These men have been slain for us by our god. And there lies the vilest of them all, the man whose sister was my wife. E Ngatoro!' he shouted as he strode toward the body of his enemy, 'was it you who said I should be frizzled on the stones from Maketu? You did not know I knew? And now you'll frizzle here on Waikorora's stones.' The horrid corpse lay still, its tongue protruding from its mouth, its eyes rolled up, its ears not hearing what Manaia said. And while Manaia gloated, his men behind him were picking their way among the other corpses, choosing what joints they fancied eating most. 'I'll have this leg,' said one. 'This tender shoulder is for me,' said another, and they put their marks to stake their claims.

But Ngatoro, not dead, was all this time intoning karakia beneath his breath, and in the bushes close at hand his priests were watching Manaia and Manaia's priests. The latter now stepped forward, and were about to begin a ritual of thanks, when the signal was given. Ngatoro's priests rushed out with yells that sounded like the dead come back. Stiff horror froze Manaia's priests and all his men—but not the chief himself, who slipped away. The priests were the first to fall. Their heads were split open before they even knew that living men had struck them. Behind them, the dead men in the oven-pits rose up with ghastly screams and soon disposed of all the rest. But they failed to seize Manaia. He escaped to the safety of the pa, and the attackers followed after. 'When your enemy is beaten in the field then take his village,' says the proverb. Ngatoro's men rushed into Whaitiri kapapa as if it were a house left open to receive them, and committed dreadful slaughter there. They cooked the bodies of the people and devoured them all. But Manaia had escaped them. He got away to round up men from other villages of his tribe.

The name that is given to that battle is Ihumotomotokia, or the battle of Bashed Noses.

When the slaughter and the horrid meal were over and the village was in silence, the departing guests went around setting fire to all the roofs. And then, with parcels of meat done up for the journey home, they made for their canoe—not knowing that Manaia had already raised a scratch force from other villages and was not far behind them. They crossed a stream that was on their way, and reached Tara i whenua and their own canoe. They were dragging it down to the beach when Ngatoro felt thirsty, from his meal. 'We have no water!' he shouted, and remembered that the gourds had not been filled since they arrived. So Rangitu at once volunteered to run back to the stream. He took the canoe's big calabash and raced off through the bush, he knelt down at the stream, and held the neck below the water. He did not know that at that moment Manaia and his new supporters had reached the other side. By one of them a spear was thrown. Rangitu saw nothing, but he heard the weapon whizzing through the air. As quick as thought he whipped out the gourd and held it above his head, and saved his life. The spear smashed the gourd to pieces, and Rangitu was away like the wind, with his head a little wet and the neck of the gourd left in his hand. There was then a frantic chase. Rangitu raced through the bush with nothing to impede him; Manaia's men splashed through the stream and followed him by easier paths that were known to them. Rangitu reached his people just in time to warn them, and to seize a weapon for himself. They all formed up around the canoe and prepared to resist whatever might be coming. The attackers emerged, and rushed upon Ngatoro's party. The 'first fish' fell to Rangitu himself, who was the first in line. Then Tangaroa was soon among the enemy, and he slew the second man. Manaia's force, being hurriedly got together and also out of breath, was no match at all for Ngatoro's warriors, who had feasted well on good roast flesh and were in condition for the fight. The scratch-force was easily broken up and put to flight, and many were slain, but among them not Manaia. He escaped once more, and retired the way he came, his black heart filled with hatred and vengeful thoughts. The name given to this battle was Tara i whenua kura, after the place where it occurred.

So the invaders went elsewhere for their water. And having taken aboard still more supplies of human flesh, they returned to this country and to Maketu, and lived quietly there, and cultivated their kumara plots.

Ngatoro himself went out to Motiti, his favourite home, and built himself the pa named Matarehua, a large carved house called Tai maihi o Rongo, or Rongo's Carved House by the Sea, and a large underground store for his kumara called Te Marihope, or The Tail-feathers. And there he lived into his old age with his wife and one or two of his relations who shared his liking for living away from the mainland.

But at last, one day, Manaia came to Motiti. After his defeats at Ihumotomotokia and Tara i whenua, Manaia made his preparations far more thoroughly. Over a period he raised an enormous force, and trained them properly in every aspect of invasion. He built a fleet of large canoes, he held elaborate exercises on land, and a series of practice landings on the shore with mock defenders. By rigorous training, and by rejecting all but the strongest men, he built up a force that he knew could dispose of anything that Ngatoro might rally to his side. Only then did Manaia provision his canoes and sail.

One evening Ngatoro and his aged wife were sitting peacefully on the long threshold of their house on Motiti, when they saw this fleet approach from the open sea. There were more canoes than Ngatoro could count, and a host of warriors ready to spring out fully armed. They pulled toward the landing place as daylight was going, and lay on their paddles there.

Manaia, seeing Ngatoro at his house, called out: 'Well, brother-in-law—here we are, as you see. Come out here if you dare, and fight us while there is still some light.'

Ngatoro stood up boldly, and although he was almost alone on the island he shouted down to his enemy's canoe: 'Well done, husband of my sister! You have found the way, I see. And that is a splendid fighting force you have there with you. Better than your last one! Then why not anchor for the night? This is going to be a glorious battle; let us not allow it to be spoiled. It is already too dark for fighting. Our warriors would not be able to see each other's weapons, or fight with style. We will fight you in the morning, man for man. What do you say to that?'

And Manaia, observing how dark it was on the island already, and knowing that Ngatoro's men would be familiar with every inch of it, was glad of the excuse his enemy had given him. He was ready to agree, and his chiefs behind him, remembering both the cunning and the bravery that Ngatoro's side had shown in previous engagements, murmured their support.

'You are right,' Manaia shouted back. 'It is already dark. But tomorrow, Ngatoro, you will make acquaintance with the red-hot stones of Waikorora. We have them with us. Do you see?' and he held up a heavy cooking-stone for Ngatoro to see.

'Then you had better drop your anchors in the bay over there,' Ngatoro answered, pointing to the anchorage and ignoring the stone. So Manaia's army paddled off, and lost no time before dark in preparing their last meal before the battle.

Then the old priest went to his tuaahu, and he spent the early part of the night saying powerful incantations that were only used in times of special need. His wife went with him, and together they performed enchantments to save them from the host that was anchored off Motiti. They called on certain gods to protect themselves, and when they had done this, they called on other gods to send a storm that would destroy Manaia's fleet.

Meanwhile, out in the canoes, Manaia's men were singing hateful songs, and laughing and enjoying themselves with reckless confidence, being certain that in the morning they would easily beat Ngatoro's force. While her husband carried out sacred rites that no woman may ever see, Ngatoro's wife could hear their singing. She heard insulting songs directed at Ngatoro and herself, with cruel taunts that spoke of frizzling flesh and crackling skin, of singeing hair, of tender hearts and lungs, and the red-hot stones of Waikorora. When she told her husband what she heard, the priest stood up and threw off his cloak, and in a sacred trance he cried out to Tawhiri matea to send the greatest of his storms, to Whiro to send his lightning, and to Tangaroa, god of all the fishes, to be ready to devour Manaia in the sea.

Then, in the middle space between the beginning of the night and the beginning of the day, those two old people heard the winds arrive. They retired to their sleeping mats and listened while a ferocious storm blew up that tore at the thatch and rafters of their roof and whistled through the reedy walls. It whipped the trees, it brought the long rain pelting down, it howled from the sky, and it lashed the sea to mountains. The sea came thundering on the rocks, and the lightning lit a frightful scene. Manaia's men were surprised in their sleep by the swiftness of the storm, and while the old priest and his wife lay safe and contented in his well-built house, he heard the screams and hopeless shouts of a thousand drowning men. All that they did to save themselves was useless. Their anchors were dragged like paltry sinkers, their frantic paddling was as nothing against the wind and the waves, and all their canoes were lifted up and dashed against Motiti's rocks. Before very long it was all up with Manaia and his men.

When morning broke the storm had passed, the surf was quieter, and Ngatoro's wife went out to see what had become of the invading fleet. She found their smashed canoes, their paddles and their spears and clubs, their clothing and provisions for the voyage all scattered along the shore with the piles of driftwood, seaweed, and froth. Their cloaks, their bailers, their feathered headgear, lay strewn above high water mark, their cracked canoes were filled with sand and bits of shell. But of the men themselves not anything remained but whitened bones, and the nails of their hands and feet, all white and pale with long immersion in the sea. So thoroughly had the progeny of Tangaroa done their work, that the flesh of a whole one thousand men was nibbled from their skeletons. Manaia himself had alone escaped those fishes' teeth. Of him, Ngatoro found a shoulder and an arm still clothed in flesh, which he recognized by the tattoo marks of that departed chief. And this he later cooked that day, on red-hot stones from Maketu.

To the storm that completed the avenging of Manaia's curse, Ngatoro gave the name Te Aputahi a Pawa, the Sweeping Squall of Pawa. The slaughter of Manaia's men by the storm, the waves, and the fishes, was called Maikuku tea, White fingernails.

Hatupatu, the youngest of four brothers, had certain marvellous adventures in the inland forest region. He was nurtured by the bird-woman Kura ngaituku, but later caused her death. It was Hatupatu, not his brothers, who at last avenged the burning of the Arawa.

THE ADVENTURES OF HATUPATU

HATUPATU'S parents lived on Mokoia, the island in the middle of lake Rotorua. They had three older sons, whose names were Hanui, Haroa, and Karika. The adventures of Hatupatu, who was his mother's favourite child, took place in the days when Tama te kapua and his followers were living at Moehau, and Ihenga and his followers were settled in the district around lake Rotorua.

One day in the summer when the puriri berries were ripe and the pigeons had such heavy crops that they could hardly fly, the three elder brothers set out on a bird-snaring expedition, taking Hatupatu with them to do their menial work. They made their camp in the district between lakes Taupo and Rotorua, and went out from it each day with their spears and snares to Whakamaru, Maro, Tuata, Tutukau, Tuaropaki, Hauhungaroa, Horohoro, and all those places. They enjoyed this work, which they did at the same time every year, but they never shared the fun of it with Hatupatu. As soon as they got him away from his mother they just made use of him. They made him mind the camp all day, and fetch their water and firewood. They also made him do all the plucking of the birds, which they were making into huahua, potting them in their fat in gourds and in patua, or baskets made of totara bark. Toward evening of each hunting day they came into camp with their catch of dead birds drooping from their shoulders, and prepared a man-sized meal; but they never gave their brother any of the nicest things they got. They took the tenderest birds themselves, and gave him all the lean and tough ones. So at every meal-time he was crying while he ate, and he tried to hide his feelings by sitting on the smoky side of the fire, pretending it was the smoke that made him cry.

After a while his brothers' unkindness became too much for Hatupatu. Left alone all day to mind the camp and the whata they had built to hold the gourds and patua, he was miserable, and felt like eating something nice. So he climbed up into the whata and took a gourd, and started eating huahua to his heart's content. He had some cooked fern-root to go with it, and he lay back to enjoy himself. When he had scraped the last bit of fat from the last of the gourds he started on the patua, and he ate the lot. Then he went round making havoc of the camp. He put footmarks of different sizes on the ground, he knocked things over, he scattered the patua and the gourds, and finally he gave himself a bruise or two on the head and some gashes with a spear. Then he lay down near the hut and tried to sleep off his meal.

When the brothers came back and found him so badly hurt, they did not need to be told that a plundering party had been there. Their huahua gone, their fern-root paste used up, footprints of people everywhere, and their little brother lying on the ground holding his stomach and groaning with pain—they could see what had happened for themselves. So they melted some fat from that day's catch and rubbed it on his wounds, and got him back to normal.

Next day they started again, enjoying the hunt and keeping the best things for themselves, making Hatupatu do the work and giving him the oldest and toughest birds to eat, as previously. So every evening he sat on the smoky side of the fire while his brothers laughed and teased him because he would not learn about the smoke that made him cry. Very soon Hatupatu did exactly as he had done before. The brothers came back to find the camp wrecked and their potted birds all gone. They got their brother back to normal, but this time they suspected him, so they laid a trap to find him out. After some more days of hunting they pretended to go off into the bush, but they hid themselves nearby to see what he would do.

He thought he was alone, and crawled into the whata, and out they rushed and caught him in the act; and the three of them were so furious they split his head and killed him there and then. Shivering with anger, they buried their little brother under the big pile of feathers he had plucked from all the birds he ate. For some days after this they hunted without his hindrance or his help, and when the gourds and patua were full at last they returned to Rotorua, and crossed over to Mokoia.

'Where is Hana?' asked their mother, using the fond name that is short for Hatupaṭu.

'We thought he'd be with you,' Hanui replied, unhitching the bundle from his back. 'He didn't stay with us. We came back to camp one day and he wasn't there.'

'We had left him plucking birds that morning, and he seemed all right,' said Haroa, rather quickly, 'but there was only the pile of feathers when we got back. We thought he must have come home.'

But something in the way they spoke of it made their parents suspect those brothers.

'You have killed him,' said their mother.

'We have *not*,' said the brothers. 'We've not done any such thing.'

'Yes you *have*,' said their mother, who felt quite certain that Hatupatu had been murdered. 'He went away with you and you have come back without him. You have killed my little Hana!'

So they stood there arguing about it. And since their elder sons would not admit anything, Hatupatu's father and mother decided to send a spirit to look for him. They sent Tamumu ki te rangi, or He-that-buzzes-in-the-skies, who was in the form of a fly. Tamumu went to the camp in the bush, and hovered over the heap of feathers with a lot of other blowflies, and by his exquisite power of smell he found the body of Hatupatu, still warm in the nest of feathers. He buzzed about, and performed enchantments over the feathers. There was a movement in the pile. It broke apart, Tamumu and all the other blowflies scattered into the bush, and Hatupatu emerged, brought back to life again. He puffed the downy feathers from his face and flicked them off his body, and went on his way.

Quite soon, in the forest, Hatupatu met the bird-woman Kura ngaituku, who was out spearing birds for herself. There are some who say that Kura ngaituku was one of the patupaiarehe, the people who inhabited this country before our people came to it, and who lived on the tops of all the hills until they were gradually driven from there by humans. This Kura ngaituku was as tall as a tree, her fingers and nails were so long that she used them as spears, and she had great feathery wings on her arms, and legs that covered enormous distances at a single stride. On this day she was out hunting as usual, and seeing a pigeon sitting in a large puriri tree she went to spear it with her nails. It happened that Hatupatu was on the other side, stalking the same pigeon. This woman's nails went right through the tree and were seen by Hatupatu, and his spear came through the tree at the same time and was seen by her. She peered round in astonishment and saw him there. It was the first time she had seen a man, since men had not ventured into Kura ngaituku's country before. So she caught the boy alive and took him to her house as a mokai, or pet, and they slept there.

Now Kura ngaituku already had many other mokai in her house. She was a very great bird fancier, and the cave she lived in was filled with birds of every kind, all sitting on perches that she had put up for them. She also kept pet lizards, which were tame. She added Hatupatu to her collection, putting him in a place of honour, and treated him with every kindness, bringing him food such as his brothers would never have let him see. She gave him weka or woodhen, kaka or parrots, pigeons, tui and bellbird, and many

smaller birds, and also rats, and even pekapeka, the little bats that live in this country. Unfortunately she never cooked her food, but always ate it raw, and she gave the same to Hatupatu, so that he was forced to pretend to eat, and to keep his birds until her back was turned. However, she went off into the bush every day, leaving him and all her other pets at home, so he was able to cook and eat while she was out. He lived with her there for a time, and could not help wishing that he owned some of the beautiful things she had in that cave—her handsome taiaha, her kura, or cloak of kaka feathers, her topuni, or cold-weather cloak of dog's fur, and her korowai, the cloak of flax decorated with black tassels. From time to time he wondered whether he might not safely make off with all this wealth.

One morning when Kura ngaituku asked Hatupatu what he wanted to eat that day he replied that he was longing for some birds from a certain very distant ridge in the ranges.

'Pae hea?' she said. 'Which ridge?'

'Go to the first ridge,' he answered, 'and to the second ridge. Not there, nor on the tenth ridge, nor on the hundredth, but go on to the thousandth ridge, and when you get there, catch some birds for the two of us. Those will be the ones.'

She consented to this and went off. After waiting a little while Hatupatu took down the kura, the topuni, and the korowai, and tried them all on. 'I *shall* look splendid when these fine feathers are ruffled by the wind,' he said as he put on the scarlet kura and strode about. Then he laid the cloaks on a sleeping-mat and carefully made a travelling bundle of them. When this was done he went round closing every little crevice in the house with tufts of flax so that none of the birds or lizards could escape. And taking up the bundle and the taiaha, he made off towards Rotorua and his home. But he had overlooked one very small hole, and through this the little riroriro, or grey warbler, managed to squeeze her tiny wings, and she flew off to give the alarm. While Hatupatu thought he was getting safely away, riroriro was calling through the ranges:

She caught the boy alive and took him to her house

Kura ngaituku e!
Kura ngaituku e!
Ka riro a taua hanga!
Riro, riro!
Riro, riro!

'Kura ngaituku! Our property's gone, it's gone! Gone!' And from this the little rainbird got her Maori name.

At last riroriro caught up with the bird-woman, and was heard. 'By whom has it been taken?' asked Kura ngaituku. 'By Hatupatu,' said riroriro, and so she at once returned, and to get there quickly she said a spell that drew out her legs and made them even longer than they were. 'Step out, stretch along! Step out, stretch along!' she chanted as she went, and in a few strides she was there at the entrance to her cave. All her treasures taken—gone! She snuffed up the wind, and it told her which direction Hatupatu had taken. Accompanied by the little bird she set off again, chanting, 'Step out, stretch along, step out, stretch along,' until at last she saw the small human figure and his bundle walking in front of a big rock face.

Now Hatupatu, because he was the youngest child, had been given a magic spell by his grandmother to make up for his disadvantages. He had never yet used it, and now, when he saw Kura ngaituku about to swoop down on him like a hawk, he remembered it. Running up to the rock face he cried out: 'Te kowhatu nei, e, matiti, matata,'—'You rock there! Split open! Crack open!' It did so, and he went inside and the rock closed up again.

Kura ngaituku got there just too late. She was quite sure she had seen him just at that spot, and yet he had vanished. She was strangely puzzled, and stood there scratching the rock face with her long sharp nails and calling, 'Ina ana koe, e Hana?'—'Are you there, Hana? Are you there?' But there was not a sign of Hatupatu; and all that remains at that spot today is the long deep marks which that bird-woman made with her nails. They can be seen beside the road from Rotorua to Taupo by those who know where to look.

As soon as he thought she was gone Hatupatu came out again. But Kura ngaituku had the eyes of a hawk as well as its wings, and she saw him. She would have got him, had he not used the spell once more and the rock opened a second time to conceal him. Thus they went on, seeking and hiding, hiding and seeking, until Hatupatu cried out to a clump of toetoe, 'Matiti, matata,' and when it lifted up he went into soft ground and was able to travel underneath. So he went along until he came out near a ngawhariki, or boiling sulphur springs. At once, Kura ngaituku saw him again. Hatupatu, because he used to live near there, knew the dangers of that ngawhariki, and he jumped safely over the crust that covered it. But Kura ngaituku stepped upon it, it cracked under her weight, and she went through and was boiled. The name of those sulphur springs is Whakarewarewa.

Hatupatu took a rest after this. He sat down beside lake Rotorua and laid his taiaha on the ground, and took his heavy bundle off, and put his feet in the cooling water. He remained there until evening. Then he dived into the water with his belongings and did not come up until he got to Mokoia, where he rested again, in the warm bath there. He was sitting in the soothing warmth, wriggling his toes and easing his aching back, when a slave came by with a calabash. This slave was on his way to fetch water for Hatupatu's parents. 'Who are you getting water for at this time of night?' Hatupatu asked him, and the servant told him. 'Where do Hanui and Haroa live?' the boy asked. 'They now live in a house by themselves,' said the slave. 'But what can your name be?' 'I am Hatupatu,' the boy in the bath replied.

'O Hatupatu! Are you still alive?' exclaimed the slave. 'Yes, I am,' said Hatupatu. 'Well,' said the slave, 'I and your father and mother live in one house, and your brothers now sleep in another one and only come home for their food.' 'Then I will come with you to my parents' place,' said Hatupatu; and the slave filled his gourd and took up Hatupatu's heavy roll, and they set off together. Then there was a great reunion, and the two old people started weeping loudly over their son who had come back from the dead. 'No, no,' Hatupatu hushed them. 'Let us do our weeping softly, in case my brothers who killed me should hear, and know that I am back.' And so his parents knew that it was true, this dreadful thing; and he told them the whole story, about his treatment by his brothers, and the food they gave him, and what he did and how they killed him, and how he was only saved by his parents' concern in sending Tamumu ki te rangi to look for him; and all about Kura ngaituku, and how he got home.

'I won't sleep here with you,' he said when he had finished. 'They might discover me. I will sleep in the kumara house—it must be nearly empty by now. I will be able to hear from there what they say about me, and I'll eat my food there. Let my father sleep with me there at night, and spend the daytime here.' So they did this, and Hanui, Haroa, and Karika came home for their food as usual, not knowing that their little brother was living in the storage pit. But their meals were not as usual. Those brothers now found that they did not get as much or nearly as good food as before, for their mother kept the best of everything for Hatupatu. So they beat their mother and their slaves, and they did this continually.

Before very long the news got out. The people in the village knew that food was being taken to someone of importance in the kumara house, and soon they were all talking about it. So Hatupatu showed himself. There were cries all through the village, of 'Hatupatu's here! Hatupatu's here!'

'That's impossible,' said the brothers. 'He is dead.' When they saw that it was really he, standing in the door of the kumara house, one of them snatched up his taiaha, and the others did the same. But Hatupatu had the taiaha of Kura ngaituku, with its fluttering ruff of little scarlet feathers just behind the tongue. He also was splendidly clothed in garments which he had stolen from the bird-woman. In his topknot was a glistening huia feather, and dangling from each ear he had a soft white pompom made of albatross-down. He was putting on a girdle and maro made entirely of scarlet feathers—a maro such as his brothers had never seen before—and saying karakia as he did so. As his body rose out of the pit, his brothers were startled by what they saw. For their little brother had become a man, and a man of most noble and warlike appearance. He glared at them now with eyes full of strength, the green eyes of his taiaha glinted in the sun, and all the thousands of that tribe who were gathered there were quite astonished, his appearance took their breath away. The little boy was become a noble chief. This made the people of the tribe begin to look on Hanui, Haroa, and Karika in a different light.

The four advanced toward their combat, each one armed with a taiaha, and each one holding his weapon in the challenging position, the marangai areare—arm up, chest unprotected, the tongue toward the enemy. They closed the gap between them with short quick jumps, grimacing horribly, and rolling their eyes about, not yet concerned to watch the enemy's moves for treachery. From the formal challenge they shifted their weapons to the guard position, in front of their bodies, the blade-end up and the point turned down. Their parents then stepped back, their father showing stolid calm, and the people closed round to watch the brothers' every move—for all these men were practised in the art, and their fight was bound to be a fine display. Next Hatupatu brought his taiaha back to the hoi position. He put the blade-tip close beside his ear and seemed to be listening through it, like a shell. Its four grimacing faces at the other end—the two full faces and the two in profile—were able to tell him what they saw in all directions and transmit this information up the shaft. Hanui, Haroa, and Karika did the same, but the people could see that Hatupatu, the chief just newly sprung from a boy in a kumara pit, had far more style than they. The brothers all kept lively on their feet, and watchful with their eyes. Their very toes, it seemed, were measuring the space between them.

He moved into the popotahi position ➤

Then Hatupatu decided it was time to start in earnest. He moved into the popotahi position, holding his taiaha vertically in front of him, ready for downward blows with the blade at his enemy's head and upward thrusts with the point. When the people saw that he had assumed the popotahi they knew the fight was about to start. The other three assumed it also, as he meant them to, and advanced and retreated in short sharp jumps, their toes scattering the sand, their dark eyes watching for some sign of weakness in his moves. But something told them that this warrior clad in glistening kura, a chief whom they had never known, was more than a match for the three of them, and they all moved warily. And now Hatupatu did a thing which they had never seen before. Abandoning the popotahi himself, he adopted the low guard of Te Otane, which is only used by experts—men who can flick their taiaha with the lightness of a fantail in the air. He turned his blade toward the left, thus leaving his chest exposed, but crossed his hands as he did so, making his opponents think he was an easy mark for the straight-out whitipu, or down-stroke with the blade. He knew they were all right-handed, and it acted as he meant it to. First Karika sprang forward and tried the whitipu; but as his blade came downward from the left, Hatupatu's blade came up and turned it off, at the same time as his point swung round and ripped his brother in the guts. In a flash Hanui came in to the attack, but he used the same stroke as his brother, and this time Hatupatu's blade came down upon his head; and following through, Hatupatu resumed the low guard of Te Otane just before Haroa came at him. Haroa, too, was felled by the taiaha of Kura ngaituku, as he tried to succeed where the other two had failed, and all in a few moments those three were brilliantly defeated by their brother's skill, and knew that the crowd were against them. It was enough—they gave in, lest worse should occur.

Now their father stepped forward and addressed them, speaking as if to all, and not only to the elder three.

'My sons,' he said, 'I wish you were as strong in peace as you are in fighting one another. I wish you were as united for your tribe as you are split among yourselves, and would set your anger against those who have wronged us all. Long have we wished to have revenge against Raumati and his people, who burned our ancestral canoe Te Arawa. Long have you three talked of taking utu for that crime, but you have yet to show you can succeed.'

Then he turned to the elder three and said, in a tone that shamed them before all who were listening: 'Are you only strong and brave when you attack your younger brother, my last-born child, who yesterday was but a boy?'

This made those brothers feel ashamed, they hung their heads, and when the people all dispersed they went away with those of the crowd who were their followers, and were silent, and spoke little. Then they began to prepare a taua ngaki mate, a large, organised war-party, well provisioned and armed, to go to the place where Raumati was. While all the men were seeing to their weapons the women cooked quantities of fern-root and kumara. They mashed the kumara flesh and baked it a second time in little kits, to make it last; and they collected crayfish from the lake and cooked that also, great supplies of it.

While this was going on, Hatupatu's father took him aside and secretly taught him all the tattoo marks of the man he wanted killed—Raumati himself. He made sure that Hatupatu remembered every detail of the moko which that chief had on his face, and on his thighs and buttocks. And when he was satisfied, he uttered karakia over his last-born son so as to give him strength and protection, and sent him forth.

The canoes were now all ready to leave Mokoia and cross the lake, and the warriors of Hanui, Haroa, and Karika all embarked and paddled off, singing vigorous war chants as they went. But Hatupatu did not travel with them. As soon as they had gone he took up a bundle of thirty cloaks, all made of golden kura, and he dived into the water. At the bottom of the deepest part of the lake he stopped to eat a meal of mussels, and when he had had sufficient he went on, and came out of the water at Ngaukawakawa. When his brothers reached that place they were amazed to see Hatupatu there already, spreading out thirty cloaks to dry.

'Where is your canoe?' they asked him. 'How did you get here so quickly?' He answered: 'Never mind. I have a canoe of my own.'

Then he took the wreath of leaves he was wearing round his head and threw it on the ground, and it took root and became a pohutukawa tree, a smother of rich red flowers. Meanwhile, his brothers' canoes had been taken over into the neighbouring lake, Rotoiti, and Hatupatu dived in after them again, and when they reached Kuharua, once more he was there before them, spreading out thirty cloaks to dry. Again he took off his wreath and tossed it on the ground, and it took root, and became a totara tree, which could be seen there still in the time of Governor Grey.

Hanui, Haroa, and Karika were astonished at their brother's doings, and took note to be careful for their own sakes. Drawing up their canoes at Otaramarae, they formed up their taua in marching order, and set off toward Maketu, where Raumati was believed to be. They camped overnight at Kakaroa a Tauhu, they reached their destination on the following day, and that evening they arranged their taua in divisions. Three hokowhitu of one hundred and forty men were in each division, and of divisions there were three—one under the command of Hanui, one under Haroa, and one under Karika. No division was put under Hatupatu.

Hatupatu knew that his brothers were jealous of him, but he went to them and said: 'Look here, you three, when you asked me to come on a birding expedition with you I did not refuse. I went along with you, and you killed me then. Now here we are, all engaged to attack Raumati for the honour of our tribe, and I am left in a very bad position. I have no one to fight beside me. Will you give me thirty men?'

The brothers jeered at Hatupatu. With all their warriors around them they felt very strong, and thought of him as nothing but their little brother, as before. 'Go home!' they said. 'What can

He had thirty figures shaped like men

you do with thirty men? The only thing you're fit to order is food.'

He said no more. He walked away, and left them to think of it what they chose. And that evening he went with his thirty cloaks of kura to a thick patch of bush on a slope overlooking the ground where the battle was to be held. Before settling down for the night he began what he had to do. He gathered up supplejack and bushes into bundles, where they were, until he had thirty figures shaped like men, and on these he placed the cloaks. When daylight came, and the enemy's warriors were coming out of their village and forming up, it was obvious that Hatupatu had a hand-picked force consisting only of chiefs, all splendid in their kura cloaks, whose feathers ruffling in the wind now made them glow like conical fires against the cold green, sombre bush.

The first hours of daylight were spent by both sides in preparing. The enemy had sent out messengers in the night to call their allies in from this side and from that, to join them against the attackers. Hanui, Haroa, and Karika were pacing up and down the columns of their men, exhorting them to bravery and inflaming their feelings by recounting the details of the burning of the Arawa, at Maketu not far away.

When the three brothers had all made their speeches it was Hatupatu's turn. He had been sitting down, but as he rose to speak not only the enemy but his brothers' warriors were awed by his magnificent appearance. His long hair was tied up in four tight knots or clubs, each one bearing a bunch of pure white feathers that fluttered in the breeze and shook when he turned his head. He had so many plumes, you might have thought he had just come from Karewa, the island where the gannets nest. In this guise he spoke with fiery words and warlike gestures to his men, and when he had finished he sat down and was not seen again. But in a moment the enemy saw another chief come out, as splendid as the first. This chief had his hair done in a single topknot over his forehead, and he was wearing a cloak of kura, like those of his supporting chiefs but even finer and more vivid. He strode up and down in a commanding way, encouraging his men to valour, and reminding them of the treachery of Raumati and of the injury that man had done to the Arawa people. This chief concluded his speech and sat down, and very shortly a third appeared, a man of somewhat lesser rank, whose cloak was only a korowai with taniko border, but impressive and inspiring in his speech. When this man had said what he had to say, a fourth stood up and came to the front.

He wore a topuni, a dogskin cloak, his hair was tied in a topknot at the back and stuck with a single huia feather, and the weapon he brandished was a taiaha. He gestured with this weapon above the heads of the men he was addressing, and urged them to be as strong in battle as the wood that it was carved from. Finally, a fifth chief stood up to address this chiefly band. His hair was tied in five small knots, all fluttering with feathers, and his cloak was of large rough dogskins, all of one colour and very rare, while the weapon he flourished was a patu paraoa, a short hand-club of spermwhale bone.

Thus Hatupatu ended his speeches to his party in five different voices and five different styles, and they stood there calmly with not a movement among the whole thirty of them, so excellently were they drilled. And when the enemy saw how many chiefs there were in Hatupatu's column, and what weapons and clothes they had, they dreaded that band most of all; while the warriors of Hanui, Haroa, and Karika, who had not known that they were to have support like this, felt very glad and believed that they now had a good chance of defeating Raumati's force. For they had but three chiefs among their three divisions, and these were men whom but lately they had seen defeated in the combat with Hatupatu. But now they knew that in Hatupatu's band there were chiefs enough to lead them all to victory.

Now the speeches on both sides of the battlefield were ended, and the enemy were sending men forward to meet the attackers. Evidently it had been decided on their side to make the first assault, if possible. They concentrated their strength at first on the division commanded by Hanui, and this part of the proceedings was soon concluded, for with a shower of light throwing-spears and a charge with the longer heavy spears, they made Hanui's men give ground. A part of the enemy wheeled at once and fell next on Haroa's men. These were alarmed at what they had just observed, and when they were ordered to charge, all they could do was poke their heads forward and make grimaces, they did not move from where they were. In a moment the enemy were on them, they broke up in disorder and ran away, leaving the enemy to charge the third division, that of Karika. Now Karika's men were doubly frightened, since already two divisions like their own had been put on the run, and the enemy could see this fear in their faces, and rushed in with greater confidence. Alas for Karika, for Hanui, for Haroa—all of their divisions broke and fled before Raumati's warriors in this battle! It made no difference how many men they had, they all lacked courage, because their leaders had not courage to instil them with; thus all that the enemy saw of them was the backs of their heads as they ran away.

But now it was the turn of Hatupatu's shining chiefs, who all this time had sat still where they were, unmoved and unafraid. The enemy were ordered to attack them now. They rushed across the low ground, and for some part of the distance neither side could see the other. While this was happening the men from the broken ranks of Hanui, Haroa, and Karika wheeled round through the bush to where Hatupatu was, to seek the leadership of his thirty chiefs and of Hatupatu himself. When he saw them coming he rose up and waved them onward with his taiaha. Their hearts were gladdened to see him, and all soon rallied to his side and formed up in good order, ready to support this chief with bravery.

At last the enemy appeared below them, and one of their chiefs, named Karika like the other, rushed straight up to Hatupatu and tried to spear him. But Hatupatu, armed with the taiaha of Kura ngaituku, turned that spear aside and struck the man down, and he died without a struggle, in full view of his own men and those who were now behind Hatupatu. Then Hatupatu drew out his patu, and with swift strokes he hacked off the head of Karika, and with a terrible grimace he held it dripping, by the hair. This terrified the enemy's ranks. They knew that thirty such chiefs were pitted against them, and for the first time they were seen to pause. As Hatupatu turned to urge on the men behind him, a shiver of fright ran through the enemy. And his brothers' deserters, filled with courage, rushed down on the foe and slew them by the thousands.

While his brothers and their men were thus engaged, Hatupatu hurried about looking for Raumati. He found him by the tattoo marks that his father had taught him on Mokoia, and caught him there on the battlefield and killed him, and hacked off his head

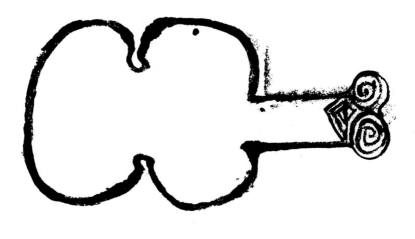

Patu

with his patu. But he hid this head, and said not a word of having killed the man they sought.

After the slaughter the avenging force retired to its camp, and cooked the bodies of their enemies, and ate their hearts and lungs and all the choicest parts. The heads, they smoked and carefully preserved, and speeches were made, boasting of having killed the chief Raumati; for it was certain that his head must be among those they had, since none of the enemy's chiefs had got away.

And so they returned to Rotorua, carrying with them many baskets of human flesh to eat at home and share with their families,

15

and many prisoners as well, for the women to kill in payment for their husbands lost in battle. When they crossed the lake, Hatupatu travelled with them. As the canoes approached the shore of their home to the sound of victory chants, the brothers saw their father waiting for them on the beach. They stopped the singing, and the warriors rested on their paddles to let the canoes glide softly in.

'Which of you brings Raumati's head?' the old man called across the water.

'I do,' cried one of the brothers, holding up the head he had. And another said, 'No, I have Raumati here', and so they held up several heads with different moko patterns.

'Alas,' said their father, 'Raumati has escaped us once again.'

Then Hatupatu stood up in his canoe. At his feet was a whole basketful of enemy heads, a tumbled mass of blood and hair and rolling eyeballs. Hatupatu spoke a karakia over this basket while holding up the head of Karika, whom all had seen him slay. Then suddenly from underneath his scarlet cloak he drew another head and held it up before his father, who knew the face and its moko designs at once.

'There!' shouted Hatupatu, 'I have Raumati's head! He did not escape us this time. I saw to that!' And a great cry of triumph and relief went up from all the men. Hatupatu's father flung off his cloak and splashed into the lake, and stood there softly muttering a prayer of thanks to the gods. When he had done this he promoted in honour his last-born son, Hatupatu, and debased in rank his eldest sons.

In this manner was payment taken at last for the burning of the Arawa, and the descendants of Tama te kapua moved from there and came to live in Pakotore; and Rangitihi was born there, and his children, and one of them came to Rangi whaka kapua, and settled there; and afterwards one of his daughters went to the Whakatohea tribe, at Opotiki. After that, Rangitihi and all his sons went to Ahuriri to avenge the death of the husband of Rongo mai papa, and she was given up to them as a reward. Then Uenuku kopako grew up to manhood and started visiting all the people who were subject to him at Whakamaru, at Maroa, Tutukau, and Tuata, and while going back and forth between those places and Pakotore he lost his dog, the name of which was Potaka tawhiti (the same as the dog that Toi ate in Hawaiki), on the island of Mokoia. It was killed there by Mataaho and Kawaarero. He came back to look for it, and when he found it had been killed a great war was begun against the Rotorua people, and some were slain on each side. After this Rangi te aorere, the son of Rangi whaka eke au, grew up to manhood, and in his time they attacked and took Mokoia. Rotorua was conquered by the sons of Rangitihi, who kept it until the tribe increased very greatly there and spread throughout the country. And the descendants of Ngatoro i rangi also multiplied there, and some of them live at Rotorua at the present day, and show the visitors around. And Tumakoha begat Tarawhai, and Te Rangi takaroro was one of his sons; his second son was Tarewa, and his third was Taporahitaua. . . .

THE SOURCES AND THE BACKGROUND

THE SOURCES
AND THE BACKGROUND

THAT the myths and legends of the Maori were collected at all, at a time when it was still possible to get them in good condition, is owed to a remarkable young man, the scholar-governor Captain Grey, whom the British Government sent out to New Zealand suddenly in 1845.

The tribes were in rebellion, the Queen's troops under attack, and more disturbances expected. Arriving, at the age of 32, to deal with an angered native people who were as skilled in oratory as they were in warfare, Grey soon perceived, as he has written, 'that I could neither successfully govern, nor hope to conciliate, a numerous and turbulent people, with whose language, manners, customs, religion, and modes of thought I was quite unacquainted'. He wished to understand their grievances, but he found that the chiefs he had to deal with, in their speeches to him or in letters, made constant allusion to Maori poetry, proverbs, and mythology. Although 'the most important parts of their communications were embodied in these figurative forms', his interpreters were unable to explain them.

Some governors would have sent for more muskets. Grey reached for his culture. He decided that in order to govern, he had better collect and study the legends and the poetry; and that is how he came to publish, in London in 1854, the book now called *Nga mahi a nga tupuna* (The Deeds of the Ancestors), a collection in the Maori language of myths, legends, and other stories, all of which, he said, were either written down from the dictation of their principal chiefs and high priests, or had been compiled from manuscripts written by chiefs. The text of that book was in Maori, lost its own link with the story of Rata—an error that has been assiduously copied by the publishers of subsequent editions, even as recently as 1956.

By chance, some correction of these faults in Grey's book was provided simultaneously by the missionary Richard Taylor, who described the Maori mythology in his *Te Ika a Maui, or New Zealand and its Inhabitants*, also published in London in 1855. Although Taylor did suppress some part of the Tawhaki cycle ('a great part of which will not bear repeating') his text enables some broken links elsewhere to be repaired; it clarifies certain points that were missed by Grey, and above all it makes quite plain the meaning of the crucial 'threshold passage' which is the climax of the Maui cycle.

Some thirty years later there were published in New Zealand the six volumes of John White's erratic but indispensable *Ancient History of the Maori, his Mythology and Traditions* (Wellington, 1887), containing, in both English and Maori, many different tribal versions of the myths and canoe traditions.

These three works—Grey, Taylor, and to a lesser extent John White—are the sources of all the stories in this book. But I have also made use of the relevant chapters in Elsdon Best's descriptive work *The Maori* (Wellington, 1924), and drawn much ethnological detail and clarification from Sir Peter Buck's *The Coming of the Maori* (Wellington, 1949). With few exceptions, Maori words in the text follow the form laid down in the official, 1957 edition of H. W. Williams's *Dictionary of the Maori Language*. Compound names are split according to no consistent rule, but merely so as to help the reader toward an approximately correct pronunciation.

★   ★   ★

In the stories which this book contains the treatment of original sources has had to vary greatly from one part to another because of their varying condition. Presenting the mythology of the Maori in the English language today is rather like trying to reconstruct a Maori village, complete with its people and its dogs, from all the carvings and artifacts and garments that are preserved in our museums, having survived with varying success the process of repudiation and neglect, the accidents of preservation by collectors and by swamps, the efforts of earlier restorers.

In the material collection we have handsome artifacts that once belonged to chiefs, their women, or their households. Weapons and implements, well worn by the hands that wielded them, have survived intact, with feather boxes, personal ornaments of greenstone, cooking gear and children's toys; while houseposts carved with human figures have survived as well, wanting only two round pieces of paua shell to restore the glint to the eyes of some ancestral god. Other crafts have survived in other ways, and so made it possible to reconstruct some semblance of a Maori house, albeit without the smells it must have contained, or all the spiders and the smoke, or the sounds of Maori singing, now almost wholly lost. Since this kind of thing is permissible in museums, where huge canoes, their epic motion stilled for ever, now float above linoleum, I have taken the view that it is equally permissible with the legends—*always provided* that the original texts remain available for inspection in their authentic (that is, collected) form; and on the understanding that where liberties are taken it is to *draw attention* to certain features of those originals, not to supplant them.

These liberties have been taken by, as it were, an imaginary tohunga tauira (the term means 'religious expert') whose range of knowledge exceeds somewhat the knowledge of any Maori priest. He admits, as no true tohunga ever did, different versions of a tale from different tribes, and has sometimes combined them; he is aware of the psychological implications of his myths, without intending to obtrude them; he is even aware that in Maui tikitiki a Taranga there is something of Prometheus, something of Dr. Faustus, and something certainly of Don Giovanni at his end. Above all, he realises that never again can any of these stories, whatever art might be employed, be rendered 'genuine', for the whole of that condition of life that was necessary for their belief has been destroyed. These are not, as were the Greek myths, nascent European culture; they come from a background that is *radically* unlike ours and cannot recur. Never again (on this planet at any rate) can a people believe that no others unlike themselves exist; never again can there be a people who have known no mammals but the dog and rat, for whom fish and lizard therefore are more potent images, and who have known no harder implement than stone or shell. The imaginary teller of these tales, in other words, is himself a totally impossible creation, about as plausible as one of Hatupatu's golden chiefs.

★   ★   ★

The opening story, the Creation myth, is here a synthesis, and as such is emphatically the product of a European, not a Maori mind. It seems likely that before the arrival of the missionaries the Maori Book of Genesis did not exist as a single piece but would have had to be deduced, from genealogical recitals and religious chants. The account in Grey reads so coherently, and is such a logical exposition of a complex subject in the European manner, that it is hard to imagine its being the work of a man who was a 'savage' only twenty-odd years before. Yet that is what it is. It was written down for Grey in 1849, in Maori, in an immaculate and flowing hand, by Rangi kaheke, who belonged to the Ngati Rangi wewehi tribe of Rotorua, and worked for Grey as a clerk. According to Dr. Biggs, 'No other version of this myth is presented in such a connected and systematic way, but all early accounts, from whatever area or tribe, confirm the validity of the Rangi kaheke version.'★ Grey's published version opens with two statements—that men had but one pair of primitive ancestors, who sprang from the Heaven and the Earth; and that according to the Maori, Heaven and Earth were the source from which all things originated. Rangi kaheke's own text, however, as translated by Dr. Biggs, begins like this:

★ From the unpublished draft of an article by Dr. Biggs for a, forthcoming *Encyclopaedia of New Zealand*.

'My friends, listen to me. The Maori people stem from only one source, namely the Great-Heaven-which-stands-above, and the Earth-which-lies-below. According to Europeans God made heaven and earth and all things. According to the Maori, Heaven (Rangi) and Earth (Papa) are themselves the source.'

One of Grey's first actions as an editor, then, was to remove the interesting comparison with Genesis. He did so deliberately, in order to let the European reader feel that he was listening, as the preface says, 'to a heathen and savage high-priest, explaining to him, in his own words and in his own energetic manner, the traditions in which he earnestly believes'. Since this book attempts the same sort of thing we throw no stones. But it is time the correct, authentic text was put in print; and thanks to Grey himself, that could be done.

A fresh attempt to present the Creation myth, based mainly on Grey but drawing also on Taylor, Best, and Buck, has been undertaken here. The main additions to Grey's outline are, at the beginning, Taylor's beautiful renderings of the chants that describe Te Po (actually, genealogical tables very freely paraphrased by Taylor); and at the end, an account of the supremely important figure of Hine nui te Po, the Goddess of Death, and the cause of her eternal shame and self-exile to the underworld.

The first sin, in the Maori mythology—Tane's offence against his daughter—is here seen to be, not Eve's offence at all, but something which is universally taboo. But in the circumstances, incest was as biologically inevitable as Eve's offence. And here we find, surely, a clue to the essentially tragic nature of the Maori mythology—a nature not fully shared by its in-the-main more joyous siblings from those Polynesian islands that lay nearer to the sun.

The Dawn Maid's shame was real and immense because her revulsion was real and immense, her expiation was to last for all eternity and to benefit all mankind; and it is this, the nature of her shame and the extent of her expiation, that makes the subsequent different names at different periods of her life, as was the Polynesian custom, or else in differing tribal versions of the story. (She appears under both names in Grey.) By this simple adjustment the Hinauri-Tinirau-Whakatau stories become genealogically linked to the Maui cycle and so depict a sort of 'evolution' of evil, from individual mischief to tribal slaughter—an effect which I do not think is wilfully imposed.

So far as I am aware the Maui, Hinauri, Tinirau, and Whakatau stories have not been presented in this way before,* and it should be remembered that they probably were never heard or thought of in this way by any Maori. No doubt the Maori *experienced* their wholeness without its being a concept in our sense. And yet, when the stories are so arranged and harmonised they become more meaningful at once, at least to us who need the concept. Perhaps comparison might be made with the assembling of a grammar for the Maori language. No Maori ever heard of such a thing; yet the grammar was there, in the language; and the structure is there, in the myths.

An important difference must be noted between the Maui stories and the remainder of Part One. Whereas the Maui cycle follows Grey's text with no major reconstruction, in the other stories leave has sometimes been taken to shift material about (a thing the Polynesian story-teller was always doing) and to make a longer tale by combining the attractive elements of different versions. In the stories of Whakatau and Rata three different versions have been merged.

★   ★   ★

In Part Two we come to the traditions of the migration— or rather, in the main, to those Arawa accounts of it that Grey

---

* When Dr. Biggs and the present author compared notes after this book was completed, it emerged that both had simultaneously and independently made the same rearrangement, and the same adjustment with respect to Hinauri's name. Dr. Biggs's account of the Maori myths will appear in the encyclopaedia referred to in a footnote above.

obtained. In this section Grey's haphazard arrangement has been ignored. Kupe has been given his proper place—at the beginning—and his story is followed by that of the Aotea canoe. Then come the four epic stories of the Arawa tribe, strange blends of tribal history and fantasy, which together form a short novel about migration and its disillusionments. In these the original narrative outline has been followed fairly closely—since clearly the Arawa tribe posses-sed some first-rate story-tellers—but I have made three inter-polations that seemed desirable. Where Grey's narrative skimps the details of the storming of a pa, and later of Hatupatu's personal combat with his brothers, I have taken it on myself to supply them briefly (p. 154 and p. 215), my source being Buck as cited above. A third and longer interpolation is the account of the death and burial of Tama te kapua, by which I have tried to correct an im-balance in the picture otherwise given of the Maori attitudes to death.

The migration tales are nothing if not blood-thirsty. The Maori was a cannibal, and he had a taste for what we now call horror comics. Some horrible deaths, and horrid treatment of the dead, will therefore be encountered in Part Two. But if the Maori could feel a gross contempt for the body of a murdered enemy or slave, he did not feel it for the spirit of his own departed kin. On the contrary, he mourned the dead in funeral rites and poetry of un-common beauty. But the legends as collected do much less than justice to this aspect of Maori religious feeling. And so, since Grey's narrative does seem to imply that Tama te kapua had some illness, and states as a fact that Ngatoro i rangi went to Moehau to bury him, I have taken the liberty of interpolating a description of his imagined illness, death, and funeral, and the departure of his spirit for the world below. It is based on Taylor, Buck, and my own experience of a tangi.

Lest students of warfare should imagine otherwise, however, let me assert that the account of Hatupatu's generalship at Maketu sticks closely to the text. I hope it will not go unnoticed that in

GLOSSARY

In general all Maori words are explained on their first appearance in the text, but not when they recur. This list gives those that do recur, plus a number of others that only occur as parts of proper names, for example *rangi, papa, tane, tu, tama, rupe*, etc.

ao	daytime; the world of light; cloud
arawa	a species of shark
ariki	firstborn of a family, hence chief
atamai	knowing, quick-witted
ati	tribe or clan
hinaki	eel-pot
hokowhitu	band of men; literally 'twenty times seven'
hongi	the salutation of 'rubbing noses'
huahua	birds preserved in their fat
huia	a bird (*Heteralocha acutirostris*) valued for its feathers
ihu	nose
ika	fish (in general)
kaheru	spade
kai	food
kapua	bank of clouds
karakia	incantation, prayer
karamu	a shrub (*Coprosma* sp.)
karihi	sinkers on a net; testicles
kauri	the giant New Zealand pine (*Agathis australis*)
kawakawa	a shrub (*Piper excelsum*)
kereru	wood-pigeon
kiato	thwart, of a canoe
kiwi	flightless bird (*Apteryx* sp.)

ko	wooden digging tool
kokako	crow (*Callaeas* sp.)
kono	small basket for cooked food
koromiko	a shrub (*Hebe* sp.)
korowai	cloak ornamented with black tags
kumara	sweet potato (*Ipomoea batatas*)
kumete	wooden bowl
kura	red; red feathers
maipi	wooden weapon, resembling the halberd
mana	prestige; authority; influence
manawa	belly; heart
manapau	a tree-name in Samoa but not in New Zealand
mango	shark
marae	courtyard, meeting place
maro	loincloth or girdle
mate	dead; death
mawake	south-east sea breeze
mere	short hand-weapon of stone
mokai	captive; pet animal
moko	tattooing; literally 'lizard'
motu	island
nui	great
nukarau	deceive
ngati	tribe
ngoiro	conger eel
ohaki	dying speech
ongaonga	nettle (*Urtica ferox*)
pa	fortified village
pakeha	white man

papa	anything broad, flat and hard; the earth
patu	short hand-weapon
patua	vessel made of bark
patupaiarehe	sprite or fairy
paua	a shellfish (*Haliotis* sp.)
pihanga	window or smoke-vent
pihe	dirge
pipi	shellfish
po	night; underworld
pononga	slave, captive
potiki	youngest child
pounamu	nephrite, 'greenstone'
pukeko	swamp-hen (*Porphyrio melanotus*)
purenga	performance of ceremony to remove *tapu*
puriri	·a tree (*Vitex lucens*)
ra	the sun
rangi	the sky
raupo	bulrush (*Typha angustifolia*)
rehua	the star Antares
roa	long in space or time
roto	lake; the inside
rotu	a spell to cause sleep
rupe	wood-pigeon
ruru	owl, morepork
taiaha	weapon of hard wood about five feet long, one end a light smooth club, the other a carved spear representing a protruding tongue
tama	son
tane	husband; male

taniko	ornamental border of a cloak
tangata	man, human being
tangi	weep; lamentation
tapu	under religious restriction
taro	edible root (*Colocasia antiquorum*)
teka	dart used in a game
tekoteko	carved figure on a house-gable
ti whanake	cabbage-tree (*Cordyline australis*)
tiki	greenstone ornament; correctly *hei tiki*
tikitiki	topknot
tiwaiwaka	the fantail (*Rhipidura flabellifera*)
toetoe	tall plumed grass like pampas grass (*Arundo* sp.)
tohunga	skilled person; 'priest'
topuni	dogskin cloak
tu	stand erect; fight
totara	forest tree (*Podocarpus totara*)
tuaahu	sacred place
tui	a handsome songbird (*Prosthemadera novaeseelandiae*)
tukutuku	ornamental lattice-work in a house
tuna	eel
turuma	sacred place; latrine
uru	head
utu	satisfaction or payment; 'revenge'
wai	water
wairua	departed spirit
wareware	forgetful
whakarua	north-east sea breeze
whare	house
whata	raised platform for storing food
wheke	squid, octopus

INDEX